Contents

IMMEDIATE MEDIA Co

The extraordinary life of Sir Pat
Media Company Bristol Limited

SUBSCRIPTION RATES
Annual subscription rates (inc P&P): UK cheque/credit card £57; Europe & Eire Airmail £69; rest of world airmail £79. To order, call 0844 844 0254

ISBN 0563531876

Patrick MOORE

Britain's best-loved amateur astronomer brought the wonders of the Universe alive for us all

Patrick Moore did more than anyone in history to get people interested in the stars. As the face of *The Sky at Night*, he introduced millions to amateur astronomy and the wonders of the night sky and, in the process, set a record that will never be beaten. Having been broadcast continuously on BBC television since 1957, *The Sky at Night* is the longest running programme with the same presenter.

Thanks to his passion for astronomy, ruffled appearance and slightly eccentric manner, Patrick's persona made him a celebrity among the general public and rich fodder for TV impersonations (he claimed Mike Yarwood's take was the best). A household name in the UK, where he was the only amateur astronomer most people had heard of, his books and magazine articles made him a star the world over.

Alfred Patrick Caldwell-Moore was born an only child on 4 March 1923. His father, Captain Charles Trachsel Caldwell-Moore, MC, had served in the army, but other members of the family had a background in performing. His mother Gertrude (née White) had trained to be an opera singer in Italy, and had been offered the soprano lead in the Italian Grand Opera. His uncle, Reginald White, gave up a legal career to be a singer in Gilbert and Sullivan operas.

GETTY

Patrick grew up in Sussex – first in Bognor Regis and later in East Grinstead. He went to prep school for one term when he was eight, but otherwise his formal schooling was limited by the heart problems he suffered up to the age of 16. While his faulty heart seemed to have put paid to any thoughts of going to Eton College and Cambridge University, it did leave him plenty of time for other pursuits.

He could play the piano by the age of eight, and promptly bought a book of waltzes to learn how to read music. He'd composed his very own Viennese waltz by the age of 10 and, at 13 years of age, a chance win on the football pools enabled him to buy a xylophone. The following year he gave a solo performance on the instrument on stage at a theatre in East Grinstead. Music was to play a big part in his later life, and he once said that one of his biggest regrets was not taking it more seriously.

A star in the making

Patrick's interest in astronomy started early. Hooked at the age of six, after reading GF Chambers' 1898 book *The Story of the Solar System*, he resolved to learn a new constellation each night and bought a pair of binoculars to explore the heavens. Such was his new-found ►

PM

▸ passion that a family friend proposed him for membership of the British Astronomical Association (BAA). At the age of 11, he became its youngest member and, as he proudly recalled, its president 50 years later.

Patrick's first big break arrived in the form of WS Franks, an astronomer who operated the privately owned Brockhurst Observatory in East Grinstead. Patrick was just 14 years old when he was asked to take over the running of the observatory after Franks' tragic death in an accident. When he wasn't showing invited guests the wonders of the night sky, he used its 6-inch telescope to study the Moon.

His observations of lunar craters were so detailed that he wrote them up in a paper and presented them at a BAA meeting. It was the start of Patrick's long obsession with the Moon. And not long afterwards, another trademark quirk was born. When an optician told him his eyesight was lacking in one eye, he insisted on wearing a monocle rather than a frame with one blank lens. In later life, he said he felt under-dressed without it.

Wartime service

Despite the heart problems that beset him, he passed school exams with the help of tutors and was due to take up a place at Cambridge University when the Second World War broke out. A sense of duty impelled him to join the RAF, despite lying about his age (he was only 16) and getting a friend to stand in for him at his physical examination. He rarely spoke about his wartime experiences, but it is known that he was a navigator on bombing raids to Germany, rising to the rank of Flight Lieutenant. Astronomy know-how came in handy, enabling him to navigate by the stars using a sextant when the night skies were clear. He only took the controls of a plane once during the War, when a pilot was injured, although he had learned to fly a turboprob.

In March 2011 a further tidbit came to light in an interview by Rebecca Hardy, which was published in the *Mail on Sunday*'s *Weekend* magazine. Asked if he'd been shot down over enemy territory, Patrick replied. "I got involved in things one doesn't write down or talk about." When pressed he answered "All right, intelligence," but, as he had done in every other interview, would say no more than that.

▴ When war broke out, a strong sense of duty impelled the 16-year-old Patrick to join up with the RAF. He had to lie about his age and ask a friend to stand in for his medical

It was also during the War that his passion for cricket emerged. He was a member of an RAF team with Leslie Ames, who later became one of the greatest wicketkeeper-batsmen to play for England. While Patrick admitted his limitations with the bat, he was a demon leg-spin bowler, claiming over 100 wickets per season in local matches until well into his seventies. He played for the Lord's Taverners, a charity team, and continued to take part in local matches until 1999. By then, growing infirmities – the result of injuries sustained during the course of

Patrick's passion for cricket emerged during his service in the RAF. A demon bowler, he played well into his seventies

The life of Patrick Moore

1923 Born on 4 March in Pinner to Charles and Gertrude Caldwell-Moore

1923 Family moves to Bognor in Sussex

1929 Hooked on astronomy after reading *The Story of the Solar System*

1929 Given his first typewriter – an 1892 Remington model

1931 Acquires a 1908 Woodstock typewriter and learns to touch-type

1934 Becomes youngest member of British Astronomical Association

1929 Start of Great Depression

1930 Discovery of Pluto

1932 First BBC TV broadcast

The art of Mrs Moore

Visitors to Patrick Moore's home couldn't have failed to notice the pictures of aliens with human-like facial expressions on his walls. The creatures, known as bogeys, were painted in watercolour by his mother, Gertrude. She'd started as a young girl and continued painting them until the age of 91, despite having no formal training in art. Patrick adored the bogeys, persuading her to paint a new one every year to adorn annual Christmas cards. They were often topical. The close approach of a near-Earth asteroid, for example, led to a painting of a bogey directing traffic in the Solar System. She painted her last bogey at the age of 91 but not before she'd seen a collection of her work published. The book, *Mrs Moore In Space*, came out in 1976. By then in her eighties, Gertrude gamely did the rounds of newspaper and TV interviews to promote it. When failing health prevented her from painting, Patrick stopped sending Christmas cards altogether. In 2006, Patrick wrote about his mother's art for *Sky at Night Magazine* to accompany a selection of previously unpublished bogeys. "One feels that it would be pleasant to meet them [the bogeys] – certainly there is nothing else quite like them," he reflected.

his RAF service – finally forced him to retire.

His deepest scar from the War, however, was the death of his fiancée Lorna, killed by a German bombing raid in 1943. Such was the pain of the tragedy that he never entered into another relationship. He once commented in an interview for *This is London* magazine, "I would have liked a wife and family, but it was not to be." He did, however, take several godsons under his wing – some being the children of late friends.

After the War he could still have studied at Cambridge University but was appalled at the idea of a government grant. Instead, he decided to work as a teacher in order to save up enough money to go. He worked first at a prep school for boys in Woking and then at a new school, Holmewood House in Tunbridge Wells. It was while teaching that he set up a 12.5-inch reflecting telescope at his home in East Grinstead and recommenced his studies of the Moon. He claimed to have discovered 'Mare Orientale', a feature that lies on the limb (outer edge) of the Moon. Although the name means 'eastern sea', it now lies on the Moon's western limb (the International Astronomical Union reversed lunar east and west in 1961). He did much to popularise the name, but later backed off his claim ►

1936 Has paper published in BAA journal on lunar craters

1937 Takes over the privately owned Brockhurst Observatory

1939 Signs up for RAF, foregoing a place at University of Cambridge

1940 Becomes a navigator in RAF Bomber Command

1940 Meets Albert Einstein and Orville Wright in New York

1943 Fiancée Lorna, a nurse, dies when a bomb hits her ambulance

1939 Start of WWII

1940 First flight of a jet aircraft

1944 V-2s hit London

► to the discovery when it came to light that it had been previously described by others. Patrick also studied short-lived changes on the Moon's surface known as TLPs.

His in-depth knowledge of the Moon was to serve him well when it came to establishing a new career As a boy he'd learned to type by copying a 60,000-word book about the Moon by WH Pickering. In 1952, he wrote his own book, *Guide to the Moon*, later renamed *Patrick Moore on the Moon*, on a 1908 Woodstock typewriter. The Woodstock was subsequently pressed into service for hundreds of books and countless newspaper and magazine articles. He was a deft typist and this, together with his encyclopedic knowledge of his subject and natural gift for words, made him a formidable writer. His typing skills enabled him to turn out a thousand words of first-class material in minutes.

Guide to the Moon was such a success that it was reprinted before it was even published, and ran to eight subsequent editions. Shortly afterwards, he followed it up with *Guide to the Planets* and translated a book on Mars that was written in French by the astronomer Gerard de Vaucouleurs.

Sci-fi for children

With his writing career taking off, he made the decision to leave his employ at Holmewood House. But he put his first-hand experience of young boys' active imaginations to good use by penning a series of science fiction novels with titles such as *The Master of the Moon*. The early novels were highly speculative flights of fancy in a *Boy's Own* style, but in the later ones he attempted to stick to established scientific facts. He claimed he was never happy with his other attempts at fiction: a sci-fi tale for adults and a farce, *Ancient Lights*.

By the mid-1950s, Patrick was no stranger to appearing on TV and radio programmes as an expert astronomer. He recalled one incident in 1954, when he was asked to appear on the BBC's Overseas Service (later the World Service) about the Royal Greenwich Observatory. Just before transmission, he was informed that the interview would be in French. He rose to the task admirably.

A later appearance, on television this time, was more fortuitous. During one of the regular outbreaks of flying saucer sightings, he was asked to argue the case against alien visitations in a live television debate. The programme's producer, Paul Johnstone, was impressed by Patrick's performance and soon sounded him out about a new TV show in development, called *Star Map*. Patrick would be the frontman of this new monthly series on astronomy, which would be aimed at complete beginners but contain enough information to interest more knowledgeable viewers as well.

The programme first aired at 10.30pm on 24 April 1957 and by then had a new name, *The Sky at Night*, to ensure its inclusion in the all-important *Radio Times* listings. The first show was broadcast

Having argued the case against alien craft, live on television, he was offered his own astronomy show

The Sky at Night first aired on 24 April 1957. Along with Patrick, a bright, twin-tailed comet was the star of the show

PATRICK MOORE X 2

The life of Patrick Moore

1945 Returns from RAF service; family moves to East Grinstead	**1945** Joins the teaching staff of Holmewood House prep school, Kent	**1945** Elected fellow of the Royal Astronomical Society	**1946** Observes mare ('sea') on Moon's limb; names it Mare Orientale	**1953** Publication of his first book, *Guide to the Moon*	**1957** Appears in a live televised debate on UFOs

1945 First atom bomb dropped

1947 Claims of UFO in Roswell

1953 Coronation of Queen Elizabeth II

▲ **Sputnik 1, the first unmanned satellite, launched the same year as *The Sky At Night*. The TV programme exploited a burgeoning interest in space exploration**

live from London's Lime Grove studio, in black and white on the BBC's only channel, and ran for 15 minutes. Patrick later said he was grateful to the twin-tailed Comet Arend-Roland – the topic of that first show. It had brightened to such an extent that it was visible to the naked eye around the date of the broadcast.

To begin with, *The Sky at Night* was broadcast on a trial basis, but with no objections forthcoming it quickly became a monthly fixture. Better still, it had a timeless quality – helped both by Patrick's insistence that there should be no background music during the programme, nor accompanying the opening and closing titles. The slow-paced *At the Castle Gate* by Jean Sibelius always played over the credits, except for one show in 1986 when the Band of the Royal Transport Corps played one of Patrick's marches to celebrate the return of Halley's Comet.

One factor in *The Sky at Night*'s early success was undoubtedly the burgeoning public interest in all things space-related. The first ever man-made satellite, Sputnik 1, was launched into orbit in October that same year. The Apollo Moon landing was still over a decade away, but the pace of research into both manned and unmanned spaceflight was accelerating rapidly. *The Sky at Night* was broadcasting at just the right time in October 1959, when the Russian probe Lunik 3 was orbiting the Moon. Patrick was able to show viewers the far side of the Moon for the first time.

Mishaps were far from unknown on live television, however, and *The Sky at Night* was no exception. It was during a programme about the Moon that Patrick swallowed a large fly live on air. Ever the consummate professional, he gulped it down and carried on with the broadcast. His mother, as he was fond of recounting, commented afterwards that the incident was "nasty for you, but how much worse for the fly?"

During the 50th episode in 1961, Patrick attempted to show viewers live images of Jupiter and Saturn through an amateur telescope. Not for the last time, the sky clouded over at precisely the wrong moment. And seven years later during live coverage of Apollo 8, Patrick awaited a signal from the astronauts as they reappeared from behind the Moon. At the pivotal moment, transmission switched to the children's programme *Jackanory*.

Pioneering approach

The Sky at Night did, however, help to pioneer techniques that would become standard elements of a television producer's armoury. On 15 February 1961, the show coordinated a live broadcast from no fewer than three locations – St Michel in France, Florence in Italy and Mount Jastrebac in what was then Yugoslavia. The broadcast followed the total eclipse of the Sun as it passed through all three locations, with Patrick's segment from Mount Jastrebac being a literal high point.

Part of the show's charm was undoubtedly its pre-CGI selection of household props to explain ▸

1957 First epsiode of *The Sky at Night* is broadcast on 24 April	**1959** Broadcasts first pictures of the far side of the Moon	**1961** Broadcasts live footage of total eclipse of the Sun from Yugoslavia	**1964** Becomes Director of the BAA's lunar Section	**1965** Moves to Northern Ireland to become Director of Armagh planetarium	**1968** Appointed to the Order of the British Empire (OBE)

1957 First satellite (Sputnik) launched

1961 Yuri Gagarin is first man in space

1967 Discovery of pulsars

▲ In a pre-CGI world, part of *The Sky at Night's* charm was the homespun approach to presentation

PATRICK MOORE X 2

► astronomical phenomena. Fruit of varying sizes stood in for different planets, while actors, dressed head-to-toe in black outfits, moved makeshift props across the set. Patrick put the success of *The Sky at Night* down to the non-controversial subject matter, the fact that it was cheap to produce, and a late-night time slot that didn't interfere with soap operas and other populist output. And, with his trademark modesty, he added that its popularity was not due to his own presenting talent. He often said that others could do it better than him – notably Chris Lintott, his co-presenter in later years.

With *The Sky at Night* occupying some of his daylight hours, Patrick continued his preoccupation with astronomy at night. An active member of the BAA, he was at one time director of sections devoted to observing Venus, Mercury and the Moon. And it was the Moon where his observations proved the most valuable. Patrick used sketches by himself and another amateur astronomer, Percy Wilkins, to produce a large map of the Moon's surface. So detailed was it that the Russian space agency requested a copy to help it plan its unmanned Lunik missions.

Patrick's life became even busier when in 1965 he took a part-time position as director of a new planetarium being set up in Armagh, Northern Ireland. He'd turned down the chance to become

A map of the Moon by Patrick was so detailed, the Russian space agency requested a copy for its Lunik missions

The life of Patrick Moore

1968 Leaves Armagh and sets up home in Selsey, West Sussex	**1969** Takes part in live BBC broadcast of first Moon landing	**1969** Publication of his book *Moon Flight Atlas*, which becomes bestseller	**1971** Flies to Johannesburg to observe storms on Mars for NASA	**1971** Appears on the *Morecambe and Wise Christmas Special*	**1972** Covers last Apollo mission live from Cape Canaveral

1968 Apollo 8 flies around the Moon **1969** Apollo 11 lands on Moon **1972** End of Apollo programme

the full-time director of the London Planetarium four years earlier, following several differences of opinion with the planetarium's board.

Patrick made an big impact at Armagh, overseeing the completion of the planetarium and turning it into a flourishing concern. It swiftly became one of the most popular tourist attractions in the area. Whilst working there, he also helped kick-start the restoration of the 72-inch telescope at Birr Castle in the Republic of Ireland. Built in 1845, it had once been the largest in the world. Restoration work on the Birr Telescope was finally completed in 1999. The restoration project at Birr Castle was not the last time he would try to preserve Britain's astronomical heritage. He later helped save 19 New King Street, Bath – once home to William Herschel – from demolition, and fought a losing battle to preserve the Royal Greenwich Observatory as a professional institution.

However, his stay in Ireland lasted just three years, one reason being his dislike of religious tension. According to his autobiography, he was dumbfounded at being quizzed over his beliefs on joining a local cricket club. He responded that he was a druid. His time in Armagh, though, would later be put to good use when he became a driving force behind the establishment of a new planetarium near Chichester. The South Downs Planetarium was opened by the Astronomer Royal, Sir Martin Rees in April 2002 and used Armagh's old projector.

When he left Ireland in 1968, he and his mother bought a thatched house in Selsey, West Sussex. It was a big investment, but the Apollo 11 Moon mission the following year helped secure his household finances. Within a month of its landing on the lunar surface, Patrick's *Moon Flight Atlas* had sold 800,000 copies.

Patrick was a constant presence on television during the years of the Apollo missions. He covered them live with fellow presenter James Burke – initially from Alexandra Palace and then the BBC Television Centre. The hours were long and demanding – on the night of the Apollo 11 landing, he broadcast continuously for over 10 hours. He covered the final mission, Apollo 17 – a spectacular night-time launch – from Cape Canaveral, having been studio-bound till then.

▾ **In the 1970s and 1980s, Patrick presented regular reports with scientist Garry Hunt (centre) on the missions of unmanned space probes. Prof Geoffrey Eglinton looks on**

News from other planets

The cancellation of Apollo was far from the end of Patrick's forays into live broadcasting. In the '70s and '80s, a series of unmanned NASA probes began exploring the Solar System, beaming back pictures of planets that had never been photographed at such close proximity. He was at mission control for many of the key moments, presenting reports with planetary scientist Garry Hunt. The pair revelled in a stream of surprises, such as the lifeless surface of Mars revealed by the Viking landings in 1976, and the multitude of glorious images from the Voyager missions to the outer planets.

Aside from broadcasting, he made many other contributions to astronomy. In the 1950s, he was involved in research that attempted to reveal a link between radio emissions and spots on Jupiter's surface as they rotated into view. No connection was found. And in 1971, NASA asked him to visit Johannesburg to observe the dust storms on Mars during the Mariner 9 mission. His daily reports assisted the space agency in selecting areas for the probe to photograph.

His activities helped amateur astronomy too. In 1995, he compiled a list of bright, deep-sky objects ▸

1976 Broadcasts April Fool's spoof involving gravity on BBC Radio 2

1981 His mother, Gertrude, dies at the age of 94

1981 Plays xylophone solo in Royal Variety Performance

1984 Elected president of the British Astronomical Association

1992 Stars as the *GamesMaster* in Channel 4 series on videogames

1995 Has Caldwell Catalogue published in US magazine *Sky & Telescope*

1976 Viking 1 lands on Mars

1986 Return of Halley's Comet

1990 Hubble Space Telescope launched

▲ Patrick's hospitality was second to none. He invited amateur enthusiasts to his home and hosted generous parties – all in his tireless pursuit of promoting astronomy to the public

► (clusters, galaxies and nebulae) to complement the catalogue put together over 200 years earlier by the French astronomer, Charles Messier. This list, the Caldwell Catalogue, became extremely popular and inspired numerous books by other authors.

Above all, he was tireless in promoting astronomy to the public – anyone who showed an interest was given the warmest encouragement. Many professional astronomers owed their glittering careers to the inspiration they received from a tour of his telescopes and a cup of tea with the great man. Members of the public would merely have to write to him to be invited to his home, Farthings, for a day, and sometimes longer.

His hospitality was legendary, and he was a frequent host of parties. New Year's, St George's Day and even the 666th episode of *The Sky at Night* were all seized upon as opportunities to entertain friends and colleagues. Guests were given free rein of Farthings and Patrick's copious drinks cabinet – although he would insist, usually with an impish chuckle, that the host must always remain sober.

PATRICK MOORE X 2

Unlike most celebrities, Patrick's contact details were listed publicly in the phone book. He naturally received many crank letters, often from fans with their own special theories of the Universe. The writers were thanked with a series of standard, often humorous replies – typically asking to see a full mathematical proof of their idea, which was seldom forthcoming. The letters he most despised were from bungling bureaucrats. They were immortalised in two of his books – *Bureaucrats: How to Annoy Them* and *The Twitmarsh File*, written under the pseudonym RT Fishall. Indeed,

He loved to meet his fans. Despite celebrity status, his contact details were listed publicly in the phone book

The life of Patrick Moore

1998 Guests on *Have I Got News For You* and plays the xylophone	**2000** Receives BAFTA award for outstanding contribution to TV	**2001** Knighted by Prince Charles at Buckingham Palace	**2001** Made Honorary Fellow of the Royal Society	**2002** His opera, *Galileo: The True Story* is performed in Cambridge	**2002** South Downs Planetarium opens in Chichester

1998 Very Large Telescope begins observations **1999** Total eclipse in southwest UK **2002** Freeview TV is launched

▲ **Patrick amassed an array of honours in a hugely successful career – including a BAFTA in 2001 for services to television**

Patrick's love of humour is apparent throughout much of his work. He was certainly never afraid to laugh at himself. He performed TV comedy alongside the likes of Michael Bentine, Morecambe and Wise and Jon Culshaw, and once joined the Flat Earth Society as a joke. Indeed, he even cited his personal favourite of all the books he'd written as *Can You Speak Venusian?* In it, he ponders the ramblings of mystics, hollow Earthers and a man claiming to be in regular contact with aliens from Venus. He rather generously described them as 'independent thinkers', although he showed nothing remotely akin to generosity to astrologers.

Although best known for his TV work, Patrick gave many public lectures, including three nationwide tours of provincial theatres in the 1990s. The venues were large and the events were often sold out, with the exception of one performance to which nobody turned up. Or so Patrick thought until he realised, with typical good humour, that he'd turned up to the venue precisely a year too early.

He also fondly recalled a talk he'd given in 1960, in which he'd made 10 predictions about the planet Venus. When its secrets were finally revealed by spacecraft, each of his predictions was proved wrong. He was happy, for the most part, to accept new scientific orthodoxy. When it was decreed that Pluto should no longer be a planet, for example, Patrick agreed. This despite his friendship with Pluto's discoverer, Clyde Tombaugh, with whom he co-authored a book about the distant world.

Patrick's career as a writer extended to the news media too, as he contributed countless articles to newspapers and magazines. At various times, he was an editor and consultant for a number of astronomy magazines in the UK, giving his full support to *Sky at Night Magazine* when it launched in 2005 and writing two columns in each issue. He regularly received recognition for his work, accumulating an impressive array of honours including an Honorary Fellowship of the Royal Society (the UK's most prestigious scientific organisation), a BAFTA, an OBE, a CBE, a knighthood and numerous honorary doctorates.

Lasting legacy

In Patrick's passing, Britain has lost a national treasure. He was a larger-than-life character, yet also a man of deep compassion who was exceptionally trusting and quick to make friends. For many decades he was the public voice of astronomy, raising awareness of our place in the Universe and helping countless amateur astronomers to pursue their hobby.

Just as crucially, he inspired generations of professional astronomers to solve the mysteries of the Universe, and a multitude of writers and broadcasters to educate a fascinated public about its wonders. It's through them that Patrick Moore's great legacy will live on. Ⓟ

2003 Publishes autobiography, *80 Not Out*

2004 Sets record for longest-serving programme with the same presenter

2004 Salmonella poisoning forces him to miss his first episode of *The Sky at Night*

2005 Becomes Editor Emeritus of newly launched *Sky at Night Magazine*

2006 *Bang!*, co-authored with Chris Lintott and Brian May, is published

9 December 2012 Dies at the age of 89 at his home in Selsey

2005 Huygens probe lands on Titan

2008 Large Hadron Collider switched on

2011 Last Shuttle launch

Patrick's FAVOURITES

His top astronomical sights revealed

ROB GENDLER/WWW.ROBGENDLERASTROPICS.COM

The world's fascination with space travel in the '60s brought astronomy closer to centre stage, and Patrick became a familiar face on the nation's screens. He made guest appearances on a large number of TV programmes including *Blankety Blank*, *Celebrity Squares*, *The Children's Royal Variety Performance*, *Blue Peter*, *The Little And Large Show* and *It's a Celebrity Knockout*. His slightly eccentric public persona made him a perfect fit for *The Goodies* too. In a 1975 episode, the madcap trio accidentally launch a lighthouse into orbit, which Patrick mistakes for a new comet. In another, he grows rabbit teeth while commentating on the Moon landing.

Introducing the GamesMaster

Perhaps his most memorable guest appearance, though, came when he danced in a three-piece suit on *The Morecambe And Wise Christmas Special* in 1971. The song and dance number also featured Glenda Jackson, Michael Parkinson and Cliff Michelmore, as well as Eric and Ernie.

Moore's enduring appeal and larger-than-life personality attracted fresh admirers with each new generation. That was never more true than in the '90s. Patrick was persuaded to take the title role in Channel 4's *GamesMaster*, the UK's first TV show dedicated to computer games, despite knowing nothing about them. He claimed he took the job purely for the money, which he donated to a cystic fibrosis charity. The gaming hints he read from the *GamesMaster* autocue was, to him, complete gobbledegook. "For a long time afterwards, I was besieged by young enthusiasts who wanted to know how to escape from level six," he recalled. "Rather lamely, I explained that this was classified information and they'd have to work it out for themselves."

Such was Patrick's appeal that his 1998 spot as a guest on the BBC's satirical panel show *Have I Got News For You* remains a highlight of the long-running series. When Paul Merton asked him if he thought there was likely to be life elsewhere in the Universe, he replied: "With a hundred thousand million stars in our Galaxy, there's probably another show like this going on somewhere!"

Patrick also attempted to dispel myths about a disaster in the year 2000 using a *Sky at Night*-style ▸

▴ **Patrick (centre) hams it up on *The Morecambe And Wise* show in 1971**

▾ **Patrick holds up his answer in a publicity shot for comedy quiz show *Blankety Blank***

◂ **Demonstrating zero gravity with his close friend, the comedian Michael Bentine, on *The Sky At Night***

▸ demonstration involving a bowl of fruit. "It's utter bunk. Now we're coming up to the millennium, every crackpot's coming out of the woodwork," he quipped, to knowing laughter from the audience.

He also dismissed any suggestion that he would take on the role of Minister for UFOs in a Government run by the Monster Raving Loony Party. "I can't be," he explained. "That wouldn't be sensible. If we get elected, I'm going to be Minister for Finance." He rounded off his *Have I Got News For You* appearance by accompanying the closing credits on the xylophone.

Nearly a decade later, he teamed up with Paul Merton again on *Room 101*. An archive clip of him performing The Prodigy's *Firestarter* on xylophone played during the closing credits. But his *Room 101* appearance created a short-lived media storm, owing to Patrick's comment that "the BBC now is run by women and it shows soap operas, cooking, quizzes, kitchen-sink plays. You wouldn't have had that in the golden days". The response from BBC bigwigs was remarkably tolerant. A statement said that Patrick's outspokenness was "what we all love" about the TV icon.

Clowning around

Patrick also performed with another comedy legend – his good friend and star of the *Goon Show*, Michael Bentine. Their paths first crossed during World War II, and continued to do so until Bentine's death in 1996. The pair enjoyed getting into scrapes together. On one occasion, after Moore had contributed to a sketch in which Bentine sent the BBC Television Centre into space, they were chastised in an official letter from the Corporation. "BBC Television Centre is not to be used for the purpose of entertainment," it said, stuffily.

Bentine returned the favour by attempting to demonstrate zero gravity in *The Sky At Night* studio. As Patrick recalled in his autobiography, "I have a photograph showing us wallowing around, dressed in cumbersome spacesuits and looking a little like aerial sea lions." Another 'experiment' involved the pair attempting to practice telepathy on live television. It was, of course, a complete failure. But as Patrick noted, "At least we tried!"

His comedy appearances weren't just confined to TV. He also popped up for a spot of verbal sparring on the Radio 4 panel show *Just A Minute* with Peter Jones and Clement Freud in 1975. And in the late 1970s he appeared, appropriately enough, in the radio version of *The Hitchhiker's Guide To The Galaxy*. A decade earlier he'd shared the microphone with two of Britain's great comic actors. Kenneth Horne and Kenneth Williams were among the cast that performed *Round The Horne*. Patrick's guest spot on the show came just days before Horne's untimely death.

▴ **Patrick played amateur cricket well into his seventies, taking the field with legends such as Jim Laker and Denis Compton**

Away from light comedy, Patrick entertained the public as both a musician and an unlikely sportsman. Proficient on the xylophone, he performed a solo spot during 1981's *Royal Variety Performance*. As for sport, he was a passionate cricketer, usually for his local village side. But as a famous face, he was regularly asked to play in matches arranged by The Lord's Taverners, a sports club and charity. Among the noteworthy cricketers Patrick played with, or against, were the legendary spin bowler Jim Laker, plus England batsmen John Edrich, Ken Barrington and Denis Compton. On one occasion, Patrick made a last wicket stand of 110 with Compton but claimed to have contributed just one run to the partnership.

▴ **The '90s saw Patrick in the role of *GamesMaster* for Channel 4**

50th anniversary

Famous faces were always happy to pay tribute to Patrick's achievements. One was the former MP, Lembit Öpik. His grandfather, the astronomer Ernst Öpik, encountered Patrick in the 1960s, when ▸

BBC X 2, HEWLAND INTERNATIONAL/CHANNEL 4, CHRIS WHEELER/BBC

Patrick was indisputably amongst the cream of the entertainment world

▲ **Famous faces such as Myleene Klass and Lembit Öpik (inset) attended *The Sky at Night*'s 50th anniversary party**

PA PHOTOS, CHRIS WHEELER

► both worked in Armagh. Four decades later, Lembit was one of many famous faces who attended a party at Patrick's Selsey home. The party, celebrating 50 years of *The Sky at Night* in 2007, attracted a host of celebrities including author and amateur astronomer Terry Pratchett, Myleene Klass, Brian Blessed (appearing via video link) and erstwhile member of the Rolling Stones, Bill Wyman. Patrick had been among the eclectic cast of Wyman's 1983

◄ **A friend of Patrick's, Brian May appeared on *The Sky at Night* to celebrate the show's 50th anniversary in 2007**

biopic *Digital Dreams*, a film produced using the very latest technology – an Apple home computer.

Helping Patrick celebrate the show's anniversary was Brian May, guitarist in Queen. Both were passionate about astronomy. Patrick even admitted he was the lesser qualified of the pair when May completed his doctorate in astrophysics in 2007. Together with astrophysicist Chris Lintott, they wrote a book: *Bang! The Complete History Of The Universe.*

A later landmark – the 700th episode of *The Sky at Night* in March 2011 – featured impressionist Jon Culshaw playing a younger version of Patrick and Prof Brian Cox, then recently emerged as a superstar amongst science presenters.

In a hugely eventful life that spanned much of the 20th century and into the 21st, Patrick was indisputably amongst the cream of the entertainment world. It was only fitting that in 2001 he was awarded a BAFTA for services to television. It was presented by Apollo 11 astronaut Buzz Aldrin, who flew in from America for the ceremony. Patrick was typically self-deprecating. "I must admit that I am overwhelmed. There are so many people here who have done so much more than I have. After all, I have merely done some commentating," he said.

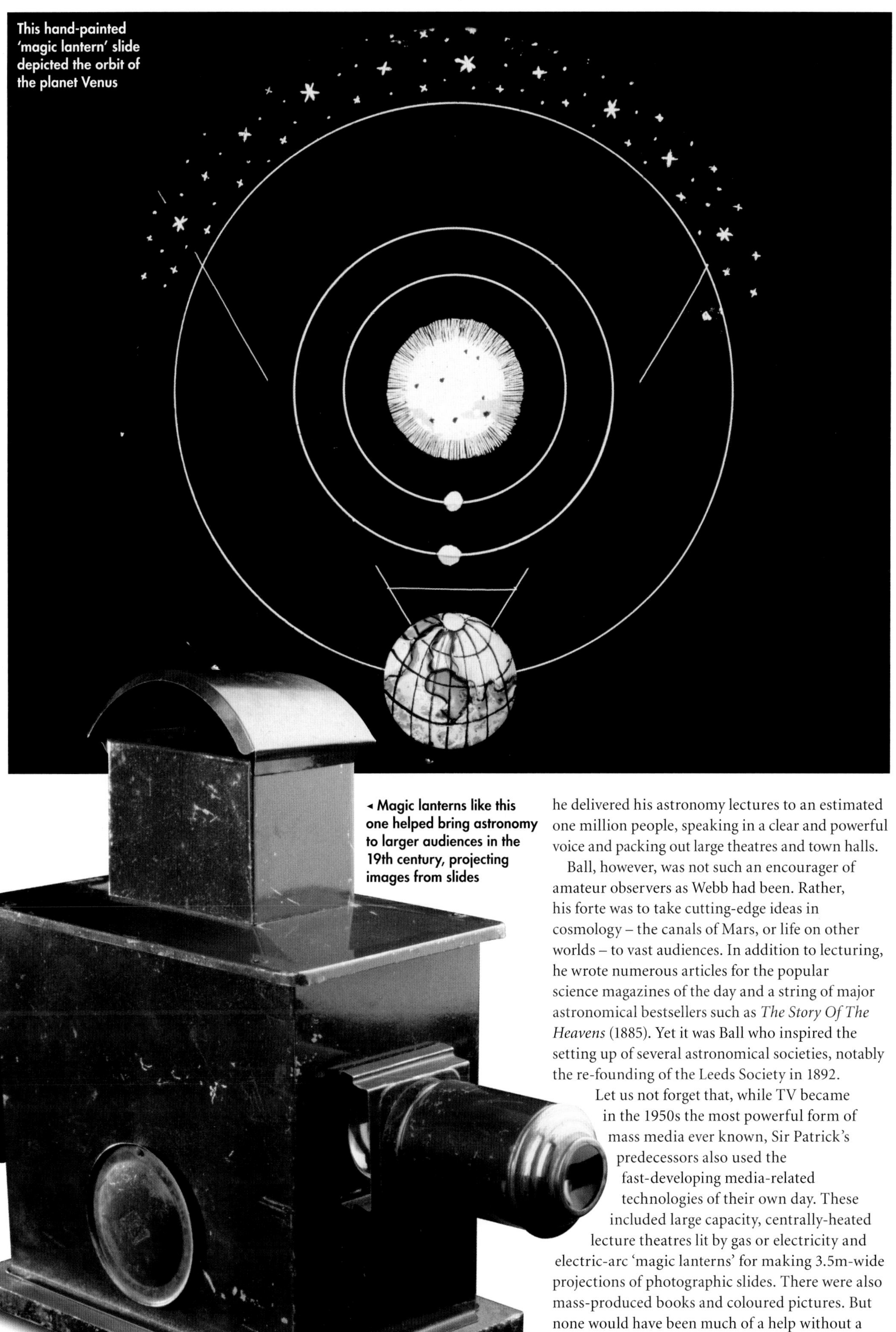

This hand-painted 'magic lantern' slide depicted the orbit of the planet Venus

◂ Magic lanterns like this one helped bring astronomy to larger audiences in the 19th century, projecting images from slides

he delivered his astronomy lectures to an estimated one million people, speaking in a clear and powerful voice and packing out large theatres and town halls.

Ball, however, was not such an encourager of amateur observers as Webb had been. Rather, his forte was to take cutting-edge ideas in cosmology – the canals of Mars, or life on other worlds – to vast audiences. In addition to lecturing, he wrote numerous articles for the popular science magazines of the day and a string of major astronomical bestsellers such as *The Story Of The Heavens* (1885). Yet it was Ball who inspired the setting up of several astronomical societies, notably the re-founding of the Leeds Society in 1892.

Let us not forget that, while TV became in the 1950s the most powerful form of mass media ever known, Sir Patrick's predecessors also used the fast-developing media-related technologies of their own day. These included large capacity, centrally-heated lecture theatres lit by gas or electricity and electric-arc 'magic lanterns' for making 3.5m-wide projections of photographic slides. There were also mass-produced books and coloured pictures. But none would have been much of a help without a powerful intellect, an engaging flow of words and ▸

▾ Wartime blackouts made many city dwellers aware of the beauty of the night sky for the first time

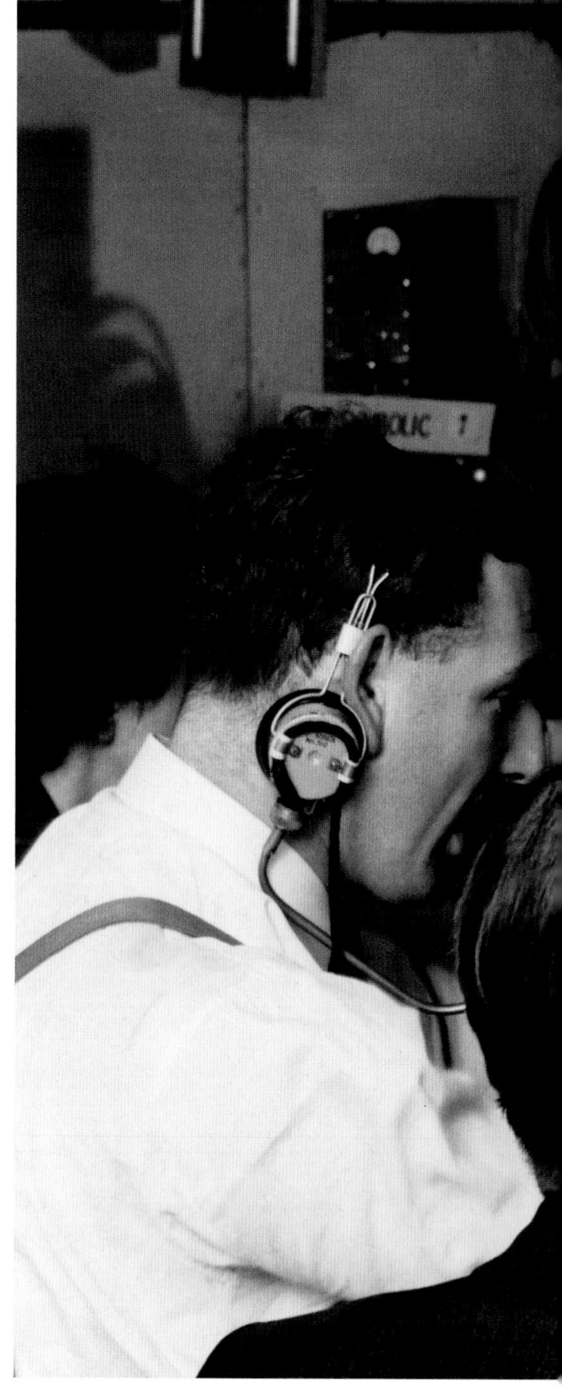

▸ a captivating personality to make a communicator's character come alive and cement the bond between them and the audience.

I would suggest that the high level of popular participation in astronomy and other sciences was very much a British, and perhaps also an American, phenomenon. Unlike in continental Europe, science in Britain and the British Empire was not dominated by universities, professors with PhDs and government departments that controlled the funding. Instead, British astronomy was paid for by its own 'grand amateur' practitioners. At the research level, these included Sir John Herschel, Lord Rosse, Sir William Huggins and even Charles Darwin, none of whom ever held a paid scientific post in their lives. Instead, they practised science because they loved it: the true meaning of the word amateur. Consequently, this absence of control and bureaucracy opened up British science to private initiatives that included extensive popularisation. What's more, Army and Navy officers were prominent in this 'Grand Amateur' world and

To present television effectively required a different set of skills from lecturing in a university

Patrick, as an RAF officer, fitted perfectly into that venerable British tradition.

Three things, moreover, were of particular significance for the promotion of astronomical knowledge between 1890 and 1950. Firstly, there was the growth of large astronomical societies in cities such as Manchester, Leeds and Newcastle, along with the British Astronomical Association itself, which Patrick joined as an 11-year-old in 1934. These societies had a major teaching role and inspired several generations of amateur observers and telescope-makers. Secondly, there were the

Saturn

"Many people regard Saturn as the most beautiful object in the entire sky. This is certainly my view. When seen through an adequate telescope against a dark sky, there is nothing to match the glory of the Ringed Planet. Other planets have rings but these are dark and obscure, and in no way comparable with the brilliant icy rings of Saturn. To the naked eye, it looks like a bright star."

Sky at Night Magazine, February 2006

WORDS: GRAHAM SOUTHORN

Patrick's likes AND DISLIKES

From astronauts to astrology and parties to powerful women, Patrick's opinions revealed his multifaceted personality

Likes

The Moon
Of all astronomical topics, he reserved his greatest passion for all things lunar. "Once a Moon man, always a Moon man," was an expression he was apt to use. The Moon kept cropping up in his life. His first paper for the British Astronomical Association was on lunar craters, and his maps helped unmanned Soviet and American probes navigate to the far side of the Moon. Later, he presented live coverage of the Apollo landings and subsequently interviewed many Apollo astronauts, including Neil Armstrong and Buzz Aldrin.

A tipple
If there's one thing Patrick loved more than a drink it was sharing one. Visitors were invited to partake of his well-stocked drinks cabinet, which was governed by the 'Iremonger rules': you help yourself. The phrase was named after Edmund Iremonger, a local independent politician whom he knew. Patrick enjoyed vodka, and gin and tonic, and once named the Greek spirit ouzo as his favourite tipple.

Cats
So deep was his love of feline companions that he described the day a childhood pet died as one of the worst of his life. In later years, he owned two: the black and white Jeannie and the pure black Ptolemy. They had the run of the house and a large netted enclosure in the garden (Patrick being preoccupied with their safety). The porch door was operated as an 'airlock' in tandem with an inner door, to ensure they never escaped their comfortable confines.

Cricket
He was an enthusiastic amateur, taking around 100 wickets per season over five decades in village leagues. His only style of bowling was spin and he compared his unorthodox action to "a wallaby doing a barn dance". He occupied 11 in the batting order, rarely troubling the scorers, and confessed to being a lousy fielder. Thanks to his celebrity status, though, he played with some of England's greatest cricketers in charity matches for the Lord's Taverners, finally retiring at the age of 77.

Xylophone
Children of the 1960s and '70s will have fond memories of Patrick popping up on all manner of TV programmes to play the xylophone, not least in 1981's *Royal Variety Performance*. A skilled musician, he was happy to play it for laughs, once covering The Prodigy's *Firestarter* alongside Jon Culshaw doing an impression of him. In the '90s, an animated cartoon called *Patrick Moore Plays the Xylophone* became a surprise internet hit.

Parties
His mother was very fond of social gatherings and Patrick must have inherited a party-loving gene. Often they were thrown on the flimsiest of excuses, including St George's Day, St Patrick's Day (despite Moore being English) and the 666th episode of *The Sky at Night*. They often went on late into the night, with many guests going into the garden to use his telescopes. The one event he never celebrated with a party was Christmas, but he invariably made up for it with a big bash on New Year's Eve.

Viennese waltzes
Patrick learnt to read music from a book of Viennese waltzes and the first piece of music he composed, aged 10, was one of these ballroom dances. His passion for this 19th century musical genre never left him; he loved listening to Johann Strauss and Carl Ziehrer, who was his favourite composer.

Monocles
It was his trademark, of course, and seemed to accompany him everywhere. He once said he felt underdressed without it. Patrick started wearing one when he

REX, BRIDGEMAN, NASA, THINKSTOCK X 5

was just 16. Offered a pair of spectacles for a weakness in one eye, he decided it was a waste of materials since the other eye didn't need correcting. He wore one when flying during the war and built up a small collection of them over the years.

Astronauts

He had the utmost respect for astronauts and befriended a great many. Few other people could claim to have met both the first man on the Moon, Neil Armstrong and the first airman, Orville Wright. His admiration was often reciprocated. Armstrong agreed to one of a select few TV interviews for *The Sky at Night* in 1970, while Buzz Aldrin appeared on the show in 2009 and also presented Patrick with his BAFTA. British-born Shuttle astronaut Piers Sellers was a frequent guest too.

Travel

In old age, when infirmity had rendered him immobile, he often expressed regret that he could no longer travel. It was hardly surprising, as he did an awful lot in the preceding years. Alongside filming for *The Sky at Night* in Arizona, Mauritania and the former Yugoslavia, there were trips to astronomical conferences and speaking engagements on specialist cruises, all filling his house with souvenir shot glasses. ►

Dislikes

Astrology
He found all things astrological beneath contempt and was baffled that anyone could take it seriously. "There's one born every minute," he lamented, and never saw the funny side if anyone confused it with his beloved astronomy. Asked if he ever read horoscopes, he claimed to have done so only once. That day's prediction for Pisces – "an outstanding athletic feat" – went unfulfilled when he took no wickets for 40 runs in a cricket match.

Women in power
Patrick's views on women in positions of power could most charitably be described as non-PC. In 2007 he blamed them for ruining the BBC with a glut of cookery programmes, soaps and quizzes. He reserved particular contempt for "jokey" female newsreaders and even claimed to have stopped watching *Star Trek* when a woman became ship's captain. That's not to say Patrick disliked all successful women – he had great respect for *Sky at Night* producer Jane Fletcher and also expressed admiration for former MP Ann Widdecombe, a fellow animal lover.

Bureaucracy
He railed against red tape and those who created it, devoting an entire chapter of his autobiography to the topic, complete with advice on dealing with incorrect bills. His lifelong loathing was inspired by a final demand from the gas board, despite the fact that his central heating ran on oil. The ensuing correspondence inspired two books: *Bureaucrats: How to Annoy Them*, and *The Twitmarsh Files*, both under the jokey pseudonym RT Fishall.

The EU
Scornful of politicians (he often joked that Guy Fawkes had the right idea about Parliament), he reserved special ire for the EU. He insisted on using imperial measurements rather than metric, and once said he wouldn't object to Europe being blasted into space because "it's never been any good to us." The producer of *The Sky at Night* often had to remove election posters promoting UKIP (the United Kingdom Independence Party) from his garden prior to filming, to ensure they didn't compromise the BBC's impartiality.

That goose egg
When Patrick was asked to comment on the longevity of *The Sky at Night*, he often lamented his absence from the single episode of the monthly series he had missed out on presenting. The only thing that could stop him was illness, and that's exactly what happened in 2004 when he was hospitalised with salmonella, contracted from a goose egg. He often joked that if he could have found the goose he would have wrung its neck!

Fox hunting
Patrick may have had harsh words for the goose that laid the infected egg, but in reality he was a passionate animal lover and equally passionate when it came to protecting them from cruelty. An avowed opponent of fox hunting from his teens, he considered the practice barbaric and denounced it at every opportunity. In 2009, he appeared on a televised debate with MPs on BBC Two's *The Daily Politics* to protest that the hunting ban wasn't being effectively enforced.

Music in The Sky at Night
There was no music in the programme at Patrick's insistence, other than its classical title theme, *At the Castle Gate* by Jean Sibelius. This was to ensure that science was treated with due seriousness, but in hindsight it was a prescient move. With no nods to fashion or popular culture, the programme never dated and retained its core audience for decades. Producer Jane Fletcher once apologised to Patrick when music could be heard

footage she'd filmed of an eclipse. The sound of an orchestra playing nearby had been captured inadvertently by the microphones. Luckily for all concerned, Patrick didn't mind.

Contracts

Patrick claimed never to have signed a contract with the BBC, saying he was a freelance employee bound by a 'gentleman's agreement'. Not that viewers realised. He recalled once receiving a letter asking him to take a pay cut in sympathy with the economic downturn. He replied that he'd be glad to, but that a percentage cut of his non-existent annual retainer would still amount to £0. Despite receiving offers from rival channels, he was never tempted to break his word by the promise of greater financial reward.

Index-free books

As well as writing dozens of books on astronomy, Patrick loved reading and reviewing them for *Sky at Night Magazine*. He typically awarded books the maximum rating if he found them useful, or the lowest if they contained factual errors. Titles were praised lavishly for having a comprehensive index; those without one were often lambasted for their lack of usefulness as reference material.

INTERVIEWS BY DANIEL DOWN

The other side of the CAMERA

Patrick's producers and co-presenters on *The Sky at Night* reveal what it was like to work with a legend

The 700th episode of *The Sky at Night* was broadcast in March 2011, a landmark few would have predicted when the first episode aired in April 1957. We interviewed all but one of the show's producers to find out their personal highlights of working with Patrick. The only one missing was the man who came up with the idea for the programme, Paul Johnstone. He worked on *The Sky at Night* for its first nine years, but passed away in 1976.

We also spoke to two of Patrick's co-presenters – Garry Hunt from the 1970s and 1980s and Chris Lintott, who made his first appearance in the new millennium.

Both cast and crew played an integral part in bringing epochal events into people's living rooms. One by one, space probes visited the Moon and planets to beam back close-up views of the Solar System. And then there were astronauts like Neil Armstrong and Piers Sellers – their interviews with Patrick will live long in the memory.

The programme wasn't always entirely serious. Cast and crew found time for jollity in Michael Bentine's garden and organised a cricket match simply to film Patrick's bowling. *The Sky at Night*, it's clear, was no ordinary job – they were making TV history.

EX, PAUL VANEZIS

▾ Left to right behind Patrick in 2007: producers Patricia Owtram, Patricia Wood, Pieter Morpurgo, Ian Russell and Jane Fletcher

Patricia Owtram

Producer 1966 – 1974

One of the challenges was the speed at which Patrick talked

Paul Johnstone started *The Sky at Night* in April 1957, but after nine years the BBC wanted Paul to do *Chronicle* on BBC Two, so he very tentatively introduced me to Patrick to see if we could get on. We were both a bit cautious, but in fact we got on very well from the beginning. Patrick always knew exactly what he wanted to do and it was really a matter of enabling him to do it.

During the Apollo Moon landings we had some really exciting episodes. We went to Houston for the press conference when the first three astronauts came back, and they brought these little Moon rocks with them. It was absolutely fantastic to think that a day or two earlier they'd been on the Moon. We interviewed Neil Armstrong in a programme on 18 November 1970, when he eventually came over to England. Armstrong was very nice indeed and easy to talk to. Of course, Patrick had been mapping the Moon before the War. It was really his maps, among others, that made the Moon landings possible.

Patrick was very enthusiastic and very loyal to the programme; nothing would make him miss a show. He is a brilliant communicator; he is just so clear, so I never tried to learn too much about astronomy. I thought the best thing was if I didn't really know [what something meant] I could say: "I don't think that's quite clear to me Patrick," and then he would think of a perfectly clear way of putting it.

One of the challenges was the speed at which Patrick talked. After one rehearsal I said, "Patrick, you know the programme is going to be eight minutes over," and Patrick said, "That's quite all right, I shall speak faster!" which is not quite the answer you wanted. We once did an episode for children called 'Seeing Stars'. It was very good, but Patrick spoke very fast and I didn't think the children would keep up. So I insisted he had an autocue, and he absolutely hated it. Patrick would normally cue himself from the visuals and would do so absolutely perfectly. So he'd always get it right, but it would sometimes be a little speedy. We didn't have a script of his words, so we had to follow him.

▲ Just over a year after becoming the first man to walk on the Moon, Neil Armstrong spoke to Patrick about shadows on the lunar surface in an interview on *The Sky at Night*

Producing *The Sky at Night* was very good fun. Patrick bowled for Selsey Cricket Club and he had an amazing action, which I was always determined to get on film. He used to teach at a prep school called Holmewood in Kent, so we decided that we'd use the school cricket team for a programme about the distance to the stars and how it's measured. Patrick could bowl, and each little cricketer would represent the position of a star. To be honest, it was a chance to film his amazing run-up – gathering speed and force and finally delivering the ball, and the poor batsmen having to cope with the advancing, great flailing figure of Patrick. It was rather stretching the point, but hilarious to watch!

▲ In one episode, Patrick demonstrated distances to the stars by playing cricket

PATRICK MOORE, BBC X 3, THINKSTOCK X 4

Patricia Wood

Producer 1974 – 1981

Patrick had an ability to communicate, to make it interesting and amusing

I worked on *The Sky at Night* as an assistant from 1967 and Patrick gave me my chance to direct, and then to produce, so I'm grateful to him. I was completely new to directing, I hadn't had any training or experience. Patrick was willing to let somebody who had not been a producer before to just go ahead and do it.

The wonderful thing about Patrick was that he would just keep talking whatever happened; he'd always think of something to say. There was one occasion when there was an eclipse in Mexico. We didn't go out there, we just took it off the satellite feed. At the beginning of the programme, Pat [Owtram] was on the phone to the New York representative who was watching the output there, and telling us when the eclipse was going to start. I was prompting Patrick by saying "Start talking" and "Stop talking." He had to fill about 30 seconds in each slot, and each one he brought in exactly on time.

Patrick was just so amazing, he had such enthusiasm; it's the thing that absolutely stands out. We once did a day's filming at the prep school where he used to teach. It was so interesting to see how Patrick was with a group of schoolboys there. He was just amazing; the boys hung on his every word. He had an ability to communicate, to make it interesting and amusing. ▸

▴ **Patrick talks to camera during the recording of an episode of *The Sky at Night* in 1977**

SHARING THE SCREEN

Patrick's co-presenters recall their favourite moments

Garry Hunt

I joined *The Sky at Night* as a young scientist, one who I guess was able to communicate because I was also a science consultant for the television news. The important thing about the show was the fact that we were able to always be up to date and get the latest discoveries. I think the other important thing was that science at that time was very badly put across, and the popularisation of science was absolutely frowned upon.

Patrick and I became very close friends and we worked very easily together. We never needed to rehearse; we were both one-take guys. All Patrick and I needed to know was the running order of the pictures and then you could leave the rest to us. That was the way we worked. If you wanted a script, Patrick would produce one, but we wouldn't know what we were going to say until we said it. However, there's one thing you'd never give Patrick. You'd never allow him to use anybody else's typewriter, because he would destroy it in about 30 seconds – he would hammer it to death.

A funny thing happened during a programme we did on Voyager's encounter with Uranus in 1986. Patrick lost his voice and couldn't speak. For five days just Pieter Morpurgo and I did it, with Patrick apparently saying things at certain times. But actually Pieter was saying the question and I was providing all the answers, so that when we got back to London we could put Patrick's voice over it!

Patrick was always very hospitable. He would always talk to anybody, and that again is particularly important. He brought science to Joe Public, who's embarrassed to say, "What is this? What does it mean?" And of course, he encouraged many young people in their careers who went on to great things. If someone rings his bell and asks to look at his telescope, he would say, "That's fine."

Too many academics sit on pedestals as high as the Eiger and refuse to talk to you. He made a huge contribution to the scientific community.

Episodes with Michael Bentine were fun-filled affairs, sometimes resulting in the destruction of kitchenware

► I suggested to Patrick that we have Michael Bentine on the programme. He wasn't strictly an astronomer of course, but he was very interested in astronomy. We drove over to have lunch with Michael at his house in Esher, and had a very interesting and funny afternoon. At one point Patrick and Michael were in the garden, trying to demonstrate something to do with the planets using his wife's baking trays like Frisbees! Michael was a good friend of Patrick's and they got on very well. I remember one studio programme that featured a Dalek. Patrick and Michael were sitting in the studio and this Dalek came along, and they both said "Good afternoon" to it.

One of the most interesting episodes I did was 'The Man Who Discovered A Planet' in 1980. There was a 50th anniversary dinner in Las Cruces, New Mexico, for Clyde Tombaugh's discovery of Pluto, which was then thought to be a planet. Not only did we film at the dinner, but we also took Clyde Tombaugh up to the Lowell Observatory at Flagstaff, which was where he discovered Pluto. Patrick got on very well with Clyde.

The funny thing is that people think of *The Sky at Night* as a 'little' show going out late at night, but it spans the globe. We were told once that a lot of children got their parents to wake them up to see the programme, because this was before the days of any video recording. So it was popular then. ”

Pieter Morpurgo

Producer 1981 – 1998

If you've got someone like Patrick then you use him on camera

“When I took over the programme I basically just kept it going. One could make it in all sorts of different ways, but if you've got someone like Patrick then you use him on camera, because that's where the value is. You could make an astronomy programme as a glossy documentary, which has been done many times. They usually come in batches of about six episodes and then that's it – they go. But *The Sky at Night* is over 700 programmes old and that tells you something about how Patrick keeps doing it.

During the 50th anniversary show in 2007, we had a link-up from the party at Patrick's house to the control room at Sutherland Observatory in South Africa. When we were filming there, years before, we asked the observatory director what the future of the place was. He said, "What we'd really like is for our dream to come true: an 8m telescope called SALT, the South Africa Large Telescope." He had an artist's impression of it. At the 50th anniversary party we actually spoke to the people in the control room of SALT. *The Sky at Night* had been going long enough that it could see the birth of an idea right up to something that came to fruition. It shows the longevity of the programme and how it can cover changes and developments.

There were observatories all round the world that we went to and Patrick's influence meant that we were always welcomed with open arms. Patrick and the programme had obviously earned huge respect, because a lot of these people had begun their interest in astronomy by watching *The Sky at Night*. And some of them actually ended up becoming directors of observatories. For instance, the director of the Anglo-Australian Telescope in Siding Spring, David Allen, told me that he only got interested in

▲ **SALT was conceived and completed during *The Sky at Night*'s lifespan**

Patrick's infectious enthusiasm for astronomy made him a hit with viewers

astronomy because of the show. So it was hugely influential in individual cases. We met people all over the world who were either young students or worked at the telescopes, all of whom had seen *The Sky at Night* and read Patrick's books. So the affection for the programme is worldwide.

A huge range of people watch it, and that was one of the challenges – to try and involve everybody. Hopefully no-one thought we were being too simplistic, and nobody felt we were making it too difficult. We'd occasionally get somebody saying, "We love Patrick, but we don't know what he's on about." And yet he's so enthusiastic about it that he caught you up in it all, so at the end of the programme you actually knew what he was talking about. He had a way of explaining things that get to the nub of the subject – not simplifying it, because he didn't do that. He did it on television and in his books as well. You might start by saying "I don't know much about this," but by the time it's finished you're so enthusiastic because Patrick had got you going. That was a huge talent of his. It's underrated to be able to impart knowledge and to enthuse people with an understanding of what can be an extremely complex subject.

Ian Russell

Producer 1998 – 2002

Patrick was able to bring rock stars into the programme

Patrick was an imposing figure when you first met him, but that's a false first impression because underneath there was this wonderful, warmhearted man. His enthusiasm for astronomy was infectious. To work on the programme with Patrick, to be exposed to his encyclopedic knowledge and to see him in action was just an absolute honour. He was a legend! I don't know how many professors came on the programme and said "I wouldn't be here if it wasn't for you, Patrick." The global influence he had is extraordinary and he's very self-effacing. He always said, "I'm just an amateur", but he had an absolutely profound effect on the world of astronomy, not least by encouraging other people to be interested and to take it up.

During the four years that I was producer the biggest thing that happened was the total eclipse of the Sun. It took place just over UK soil, right down in the west of Cornwall. There was a lot of hype surrounding it and that was the first time that Brian May came on the show, as he's an avid eclipse chaser as well as being very interested in astronomy. The world was becoming more interested too, and I thought that was really a key moment. Patrick was able to bring rock stars into the programme who were only too honoured to be there – so it wasn't just astronomers who would see it. The whole world seemed to like Patrick! ▸

Queen guitarist and astronomer Dr Brian May joined Patrick many times on the programme

Paul Vanezis

Producer 2009 – 2010

Piers Sellers had been influenced by Patrick to become a scientist

BBC, PATRICK MOORE, WILL GATER, THINKSTOCK X 4, PAUL VANEZIS, REX

"I remember a programme we did called 'The Universe From Atlantis' about the Shuttle astronauts. Patrick got on incredibly well with the astronauts Piers Sellers and Ken Ham. He'd had Piers Sellers on the programme before, but Patrick had been a bit unwell and we were trying to arrange an interview with the two of them. Piers had been influenced by Patrick to become a scientist and we'd arranged to do the interview at the Royal Society in London, because that was the only time the astronauts were available to talk to. But when they realised Patrick would have to travel from the south coast, they came to Patrick's house to do the filming because they didn't want to inconvenience him. Piers and Ken were my favourite guests. They had the best chemistry with Patrick because they were just really pleased to be there, and he was so happy for them to be there.

Being on *The Sky at Night* is a great honour for scientists and a highlight of their careers. Scientists know the track record of the people that have appeared on the programme, from Neil Armstrong and Frank Drake to Carl Sagan, so it was very special for them to be interviewed by Patrick. He was also a fountain of knowledge. To have been a part of that myself is very special."

▲ **Piers Sellers being interviewed by Patrick during the *Universe From Atlantis* programme**

SHARING THE **SCREEN**

Patrick's co-presenters recall their favourite moments

Chris Lintott

"Patrick was extremely good at keeping people on their toes and always asked the difficult questions. One of the early programmes we did was about a solar eclipse in Africa. We couldn't afford to go, so the idea was that they'd show us some footage of it and Patrick and I were going to watch it live and react. So we were watching this video of the solar eclipse with all these animals in it, and Patrick was keeping up this wonderful commentary along the lines of, "And as the Moon crosses the face of the Sun, the giraffes go down to the waterhole and the hippopotamus decides it's time for bed." And then he turned to me and said, "Chris, the elephant's not perturbed is it?" and dived down to read his script. I just remember thinking, "Okay, what the hell do I say now?" And that's how I always felt working with Patrick. You never know what he's going to say next and you have to be prepared for pretty much any question. If you turned a camera on Patrick, he immediately switched on. He had a background that none of the rest of us have, in that he was used to live television. We don't have to work like that – we often do 10 takes and snip them up, because it's easy to edit. But to him, it was a matter of immense professional pride that you get it right first take. We once pulled out some archive footage and found the first interview Patrick had done with Neil Armstrong when he came back from the Moon. We found a bit at the end when they were trying to get Patrick to re-do a question. On this footage from 1970 he's saying, "First take's always the best! First take's always the best!"

Patrick had an amazing internal clock. You can say to him, "We're doing a short interview – talk to this guy and we need three and a half minutes." Patrick will begin the conversation, ask a series of questions and then wind it up. You'll look at your watch and it will be within a couple of seconds! He'd had to do it like that in the early days, because they'd throw it over to you and you'd have 2 minutes and 37 seconds before they went straight to the news.

Patrick was the most sceptical person I know, in a good way. He cared passionately about the subject but didn't get carried away with whatever the latest thing is – a huge strength."

BIBLIOGRAPHY

Men Of The Stars (Mitchell Beazley, 1986)
Astronomy For The Under Tens (Philip's, 1986)
Exploring The Night Sky With Binoculars (Cambridge University Press, 1986)
Patrick Moore's Astronomy Quiz Book (George Philip & Son Ltd, 1987)
TV Astronomer (Harrap, 1987)
Astronomers' Stars (Routledge, 1987)
Guinness Book Of Astronomy (Guinness, 1988)
Observer's Astronomy (Frederick Warne, 1988)
Space Travel For The Under Tens (Philip's, 1988)
The Planet Neptune (Praxis, 1988)
The Sky At Night – Vol 9 (Harrup, 1989)
Atlas of Uranus (with Garry Hunt) (Cambridge University Press, 1989)
Astronomy For GCSE (Duckworth, 1990)
Mission To The Planets (Cassell, 1990)
Patrick Moore's Passion For Astronomy (David & Charles, 1991)
Philip's Guide To The Night Sky (Philip's, 1991)
Exploring The Earth And Moon (Brian Trodd, 1991)
Story Of The Earth For The Under Tens (Philip's, 1991)
Astronomy For The Beginner (Cambridge University Press, 1992)
Space Travel For The Beginner (Cambridge University Press, 1992)
The International Encyclopedia of Astronomy (Random House, 1992)
Fireside Astronomy (Wiley, 1992)
New Guide To The Planets (Sidgwick & Jackson, 1993)
The Sky At Night – Vol 10 (Wiley, 1993)
Philip's Atlas Of The Universe (Philip's, 1994)
Atlas Of Neptune (with Garry Hunt) (Cambridge University Press, 1994)
Stars Of The Southern Skies (David Bateman Ltd, 1994)
The Starry Sky (Bodley Head Children's Books, 1994)
The Starry Sky: The Planets (Copper Beech, 1995)
The Starry Sky: The Stars (Copper Beech, 1995)
The Starry Sky: Comets And Shooting Stars (Copper Beech, 1995)
The Starry Sky: The Sun And Moon (Copper Beech, 1995)
The Great Astronomical Revolution (Horwood Publishing, 1995)
The Observational Amateur Astronomer (Springer, 1995)
The Modern Amateur Astronomer (Springer, 1995)
Teach Yourself Astronomy (Teach Yourself Books, 1995)
Small Astronomical Observatories (editor) (Springer, 1996)
Brilliant Stars (Cassell, 1997)
Atlas Of Venus (Cambridge University Press, 1997)
Eyes On The Universe (Springer, 1997)
Into Space! (CMP, 1997)
Into Space! 2: The Great Universe (CMP, 1998)
Patrick Moore's Beginner's Guide To Astronomy (PRC, 1997)
The Sun In Eclipse (with Michael Maunder) (Springer, 1997)
The Observer's Year: 366 Nights In The Universe (Springer, 1997)
The Photographic Atlas Of The Stars (with HJP Arnold and Paul Doherty) (Kalmbach, 1997)
Patrick Moore On Mars (Cassell Illustrated, 1998)
West Country Eclipse: 11 August 1999 (South Downs Planetarium Trust, 1998)
Guide To The 1999 Total Eclipse (Boxtree, 1999)
The Wandering Astronomer (IOP Publishing, 1999)
Into Space! 3: Explorers Of The Skies (CMP, 2000)
The Data Book Of Astronomy (Institute Of Physics, 2000)
Astronomy For GCSE (with Chris Lintott) (Duckworth, 2001)
Patrick Moore On The Moon (Cassell, 2001)
Patrick Moore's Millennium Yearbook (Springer, 2000)
The Star Of Bethlehem (Canopus, 2001)
Astronomy Encyclopedia (Philip's, 2002)
Venus (Cassell Illustrated, 2002)
The Sky At Night – Vol 11 (Philip's, 2002)
More Small Astronomical Observatories (editor) (Springer, 2002)
Into Space! 4: First Contact (CMP Publishing, 2002)
Into Space! 5: Mars The Next Frontier (CMP Publishing, 2003)
Astronomy With A Budget Telescope (with John Watson) (Springer, 2003)
80 Not Out: The Autobiography (Contender Books, 2003)
Stars Of Destiny (Canopus, 2004)
Futures: 50 Years In Space (with David Hardy) (AAPL, 2004)
Asteroid (with Arthur C Clarke) (Canopus, 2005)
Patrick Moore: The Autobiography (Sutton Publishing, 2005)
The Sky At Night – Vol 12 (Philip's, 2005)
Bang! The Complete History Of The Universe (with Brian May and Chris Lintott) (Carlton Books, 2006)
Astronomy For GCSE (with Chris Lintott) (Duckworth, 2006)
Moore On Mercury (Springer, 2006)
Our Universe: An Introduction (AAPPL, 2007)
Space: The First 50 Years (with HJP Arnold) (Sterling, 2007)
Can You Play Cricket On Mars? (The History Press, 2008)
The Twitmarsh Files (as RT Fishall) (The History Press, 2010)
First Book Of Stars (Amberley Publishing, 2010)
The Sky At Night – Vol 13 (Springer, 2010)
Patrick Moore's Data Book Of Astronomy (Cambridge University Press, 2011)
The Sky At Night: Answers To Questions From Across The Universe (with Chris North) (BBC Books, 2012)
Miaow! Cats Really Are Nicer Than People (Hubble & Hattie, 2012)
The New Astronomy Guide: Stargazing In The Digital Age (with Pete Lawrence) (Carlton Books, 2012)
The Cosmic Tourist: The 100 Most-Awe Inspiring Destinations In The Universe (with Chris Lintott and Brian May) (Carlton Books, 2012)

FICTION

Grenfell & Wright series
Master Of The Moon (Museum Press, 1952)
The Island Of Fear (Museum Press, 1954)

Gregory Quest series
Quest Of The Spaceways (Frederick Muller, 1955)
World Of Mists (Frederick Muller, 1956)

Maurice Gray series
Mission To Mars (Burke, 1955)
The Domes Of Mars (Burke, Falcon Library, 1956)
The Voices Of Mars (Burke, 1957)
Peril On Mars (Burke, 1958)
Raiders On Mars (Burke, 1959)
Voyage To Mars (Central Books, 2003)

Robin North series
Wanderer In Space (1961)
Crater Of Fear (1962)
Invader From Space (Burke, 1963)
Caverns Of The Moon (Burke, 1964)

Scott Saunders series
Spy In Space (Armada, 1977)
Planet Of Fear (Armada, 1977)
The Moon Raiders (Armada, 1978)
Killer Comet (Armada, 1978)
The Terror Star (Armada, 1979)
The Secret Of The Black Hole (Armada, 1980)

Other fiction (not part of a series)
The Frozen Planet (Museum Press, 1954)
Destination Luna (Lutterworth, 1955)
Wheel In Space (Lutterworth, 1956)
Captives Of The Moon (Burke, 1960)
Planet Of Fire (The Children's Book Club, 1969)
How Britain Won The Space Race (with Desmond Leslie) (Mitchell Beazley, 1972)

ABOUT THIS LIST

This bibliography shows Patrick's key works but it is not exhaustive. Many titles were republished several times, often by different publishers, but we have included only the first edition of each title. Overseas editions have been omitted, as have his translations of other authors' works, anthologies and titles for which he wrote forewords. We've also left out most of the books on which he served as editor, including Patrick Moore's Practical Astronomy series for Springer and volumes of scientific research papers.

Radio Times scrapbook

Patrick Moore's career was faithfully chronicled in the pages of Britain's best-loved TV guide

▼ Aired on 24 April 1957, the first episode was preceded by football and music from the BBC Show Band

▶ A preview of the first episode of *The Sky at Night* featured in the 19 April 1957 issue of *Radio Times*

Star Quest

STARS, in our particular workaday world, tend to be people with agents, and success stories, and temperaments, and talents, and a certain unpredictability that can make them either tiresome or fascinating. But when we talked to Patrick Moore the other day about this month's stars, we found ourselves in a very different world. 'People tend to think,' he told us, 'that astronomy is a difficult, expensive, and unrewarding subject that has become the prerogative of old men with long white beards. It is in fact none of these things, and anyone can find interest and excitement in the night sky, if he knows what to look for.'

This is to be the theme of his new series which begins on Wednesday, and which will introduce each month the highlights of the current astronomical news.

April 19 1957 . RADIO TIMES

TELEVISION PROGRAMMES

WEDNESDAY EVENING — APRIL 24

At 9.45 Cyril Stapleton presents 'SHOW BAND PARADE'

featuring the BBC Show Band in popular music of yesterday, today, and tomorrow

WITH
The Three Peters Sisters
Teddy Johnson and
Pearl Carr (right)
Group One (left)
Frank Holder
The Vipers Skiffle Group
Sheila O'Neill
Ross Taylor
Leonie Page
The Show Band Singers
Directed by Cliff Adams
and The Dancers

Designer, Don Horne
Production scenes staged by Ross Taylor
Produced by Graeme Muir

5.57 THE WEATHER

6.0 NEWS
SPORTS NEWS

6.5 TONIGHT
Look around with
Cliff Michelmore
Sport—Music—People—Politics
Travel—Theatre—Cinema
with
Derek Hart
Geoffrey Johnson Smith
and this week:
Shirley Eaton
(Shirley Eaton appears by permission of the Rank Organisation)

6.50 AMOS 'N' ANDY
in the film
'Andy Buys a House'

7.15 NEWS

7.20 BEHIND THE HEADLINES

7.30 NOW
Sit tight in your chair and we'll take you there
with outside broadcast cameras
The Men-on-the-Spot,
Raymond Baxter
and Bob Danvers-Walker
look at
'Ships and Shadows'
The fourth programme in the series
Produced by
Ray Lakeland and Peter Webber

8.5 THE BURNS AND ALLEN SHOW
George Burns
and Gracie Allen
in the film
'Gracie Hires a Valet'

8.30 Bernard Miles
as
NATHANIEL TITLARK
in a series of comedies
by Bill Naughton
4—'Mr. Watch and Mr. Stamp'
Nathaniel Titlark........Bernard Miles
Jake........Frederick Piper
Jessie Titlark........Maureen Pryor
Mr. Watch........Michael Logan
Mr. Stamp........Harry Locke
Barman........Christopher Hodge
Villagers:
Frank Pemberton, Leslie Kyle
The plays are based on characters created by James Lansdale Hodson, and written in collaboration with Bernard Miles
Designer, Stephen Bundy
Produced by Andrew Osborn

9.0 SPORTSVIEW
Introduced by Peter Dimmock
Edited by
Paul Fox and Ronnie Noble
Presented by Bryan Cowgill
including
ASSOCIATION FOOTBALL
Schoolboys' International
London v. West Germany
The second half of tonight's floodlit match from Upton Park
Television presentation by Charles Scott

9.45 Cyril Stapleton
presents
SHOW BAND PARADE
See top of page

10.30 THE SKY AT NIGHT
See columns 1 and 2 and page 4

10.45 NEWS
Followed by
Weather and Close Down

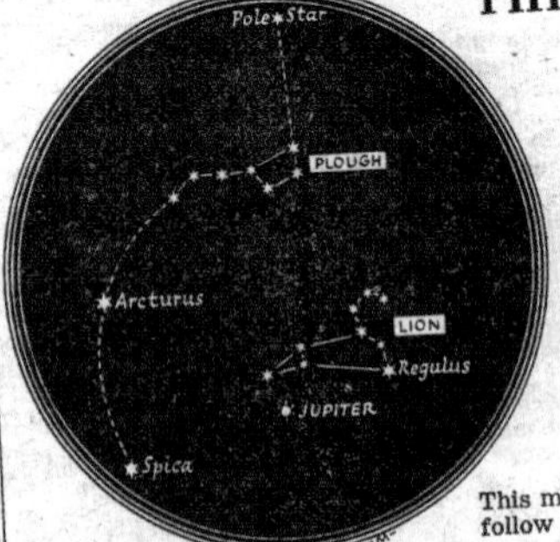

THE SKY AT NIGHT
Patrick Moore
tells you what to look for in the night sky during the coming month
★
The first of a regular monthly series
Presented by
PAUL JOHNSTONE
AT 10.30

This map should help you to follow Patrick Moore's talk

PM

◀ The 50th programme on 21 August 1961 became infamous as the sky was obscured by cloud during the live broadcast

24 RADIO

THE SKY AT NIGHT: 50th Edition

Celebrating with Saturn

10.40

TO CELEBRATE its fiftieth edition *The Sky at Night* is taking a gamble. The programme is being transmitted 'live' from the back garden of a small house at Patcham, on the outskirts of Brighton, where **George Hole** has built a twenty-four-inch telescope—one of the largest in Britain.

Says producer **Paul Johnstone:** 'This telescope is big enough for us to fix a special lightweight television camera to the eyepiece—and if the weather co-operates, **Patrick Moore** and George Hole hope to bring viewers direct pictures of single and double stars, star clusters, and the moon.

'The climax of tonight's programme will be our attempt to obtain the first-ever live television pictures of perhaps the most beautiful object in the heavens: the planet Saturn and its rings.'

To reduce the element of risk involved in a programme like this, it is hoped to include shots from another television camera mounted on the thirty-six-inch telescope in the Royal Observatory, Edinburgh. So if it is cloudy at Patcham, it may be possible to see Saturn through another telescope 400 miles away.

George Hole, who built the Patcham telescope in his garden workshop, runs a flourishing firm which specialises in difficult optical projects. The most difficult operation in making the telescope was grinding the big mirror—twenty-four inches across and three inches thick. It took Mr. Hole two years to polish the curve to the necessary accuracy of one millionth of an inch.

Although the telescope weighs a ton and a quarter, it is so finely adjusted that its aim can be moved from the centre of a halfpenny two miles away to the centre of another coin placed alongside.

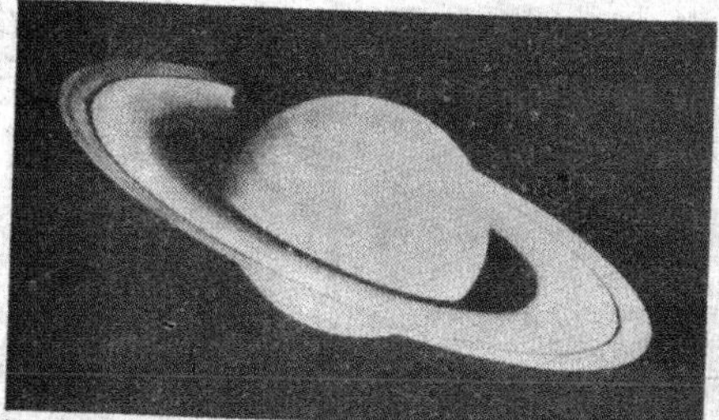

Saturn: perhaps the most beautiful object in the heavens

▼ The tenth anniversary epsiode reflected on an extraordinary period, which had seen the first satellite and the first man in space

TEN YEARS OF SPACE

On The Sky at Night's tenth anniversary PATRICK MOORE looks back

1 11.17

IN April 1957 the first *Sky at Night* programme went on the air. I had done very little television broadcasting; I had no idea whether the programme would prove popular—and neither, I imagine, had anyone else! It is strange to reflect now that at that time the Space Age had not begun. It was only in the following October that the Russians launched their first artificial satellite, Sputnik I.

Much has happened since 1957, both in space research and in ordinary astronomy. The artificial satellites have been developed into space-probes, vehicles capable of landing on the Moon, and messengers to Mars and Venus; men have spent long periods in orbit, and it now seems that the first lunar voyage cannot be very far away.

In astronomy, developments have been equally striking, if not so obviously spectacular. In particular, we have heard about the strange, super-luminous objects known as quasars, which may well cause a major revision in our ideas about the nature and evolution of the universe.

In *The Sky at Night* we have tried to give what may be termed running commentaries on these developments. Our arrival was heralded by a comet, the famous Arend-Roland of spring 1957; we were able to obtain the first photographs of the far side of the Moon, in October 1959, and to be the first to show them in Britain; we televised the total solar eclipse of 1961; we have given 'live' pictures of the Moon and planets through George Hole's giant 24-inch telescope at Patcham.

We have taken outside broadcasting units to various places of special scientific interest, and we have even carried out original research. I have in mind our 'Martian laboratory,' and the recent attempt to study the Leonid meteors.

◀ The Apollo 8 mission was broadcast live in December 1968. To Patrick's chagrin, the BBC switched to *Jackanory* when the spacecraft went behind the Moon

CHRISTMAS ROUND THE MOON

On BBC-1 and BBC-2 COLOUR

For the next six days BBC-tv hopes to cover the historic flight of astronauts Frank Berman, James Lovell, and Bill Anders in Apollo 8

THE LAUNCH

Live from Cape Kennedy introduced by **Cliff Michelmore** with **James Burke** in the London Space Studio, **Michael Charlton** at the Kennedy Space Center, Florida, and comments from **Sir Bernard Lovell** at Jodrell Bank

DURING THE FLIGHT

Live television from Apollo 8 in deep space during the outward and return flights and orbiting sixty miles above the moon. Special reports during the critical stages from **James Burke** and **Patrick Moore** in the London Space Studio, BBC correspondents **Reginald Turnill** and **David Wilson**, and from Mission Control, Houston, Texas, **Charles Wheeler**

Produced for the BBC by John Morrell, Ronnie Noble, Michael Townson

Presented in association with the European Broadcasting Union, National Aeronautics Space Administration, American Broadcasting Company, and National Broadcasting Company of America

Executive producer, Richard Francis

See page 41

▼ The 23 July 1965 episode looked at how intelligent aliens in other galaxies might be detected

IS THERE LIFE ON OTHER PLANETS?

ASKS Patrick Moore

1 10.15

WHEN the *Sky at Night* series began, in the spring of 1957, the Space Age still lay in the future. Sputnik I, the first artificial satellite, had yet to be launched; the idea of a man in orbit round the earth still seemed rather far-fetched, and the moon, as a target, was as far away as ever. The situation has changed dramatically since then, and during the series we have been able to follow the course of events step by step. One of our most exciting programmes came a little over two years after we began, when, in October 1959, we showed the first pictures of the reverse side of the moon.

On the other hand, we must always remember that the solar system in which we live is only a tiny part of the universe as a whole. In the foreseeable future, there are only three worlds—the moon, Mars, and (less predictably) Venus—which may be reached by men. None of these seems to be able to support advanced life of the kind we know, and the remaining bodies in the sun's system are even less welcoming. If we are to find other intelligent beings, we must look further afield.

This is reasonable enough, since the sun is only one of at least 100,000 million stars in our own particular star-system or galaxy. Moreover, there are many millions of other galaxies within range of the world's largest telescopes. Since the sun is a perfectly ordinary star, there is no reason to suppose that it is unique in being attended by a system of planets. Most modern astronomers believe that such systems are common, and that life is widespread throughout the universe; there must surely be almost countless races far more advanced than ourselves. What these supposed beings look like is, of course, quite another matter, and unless we can contact them we shall be unable to find out.

Yet the difficulties are immense. Sending rocket probes is out of the question owing to the vast distances involved. Therefore, the only possible way of establishing that 'other men' exist is to contact them by means of radio, and some years ago a project of this nature was initiated in America. It was not successful, but it is a measure of our changed attitude that the experiment was considered worth attempting at all. Since then there has been the sensational Russian announcement that a 'super-civilisation' has been traced by its radio signals.

Few people have any faith in this Russian claim, but it is not impossible that we shall one day be able to establish that other civilisations exist far away in space. This is the theme of the 100th *Sky at Night*, in which experts from both East and West will be taking part tonight.

26

RADIO TIMES July 17, 1969

WHAT I BELIEVE THEY'LL FIND...

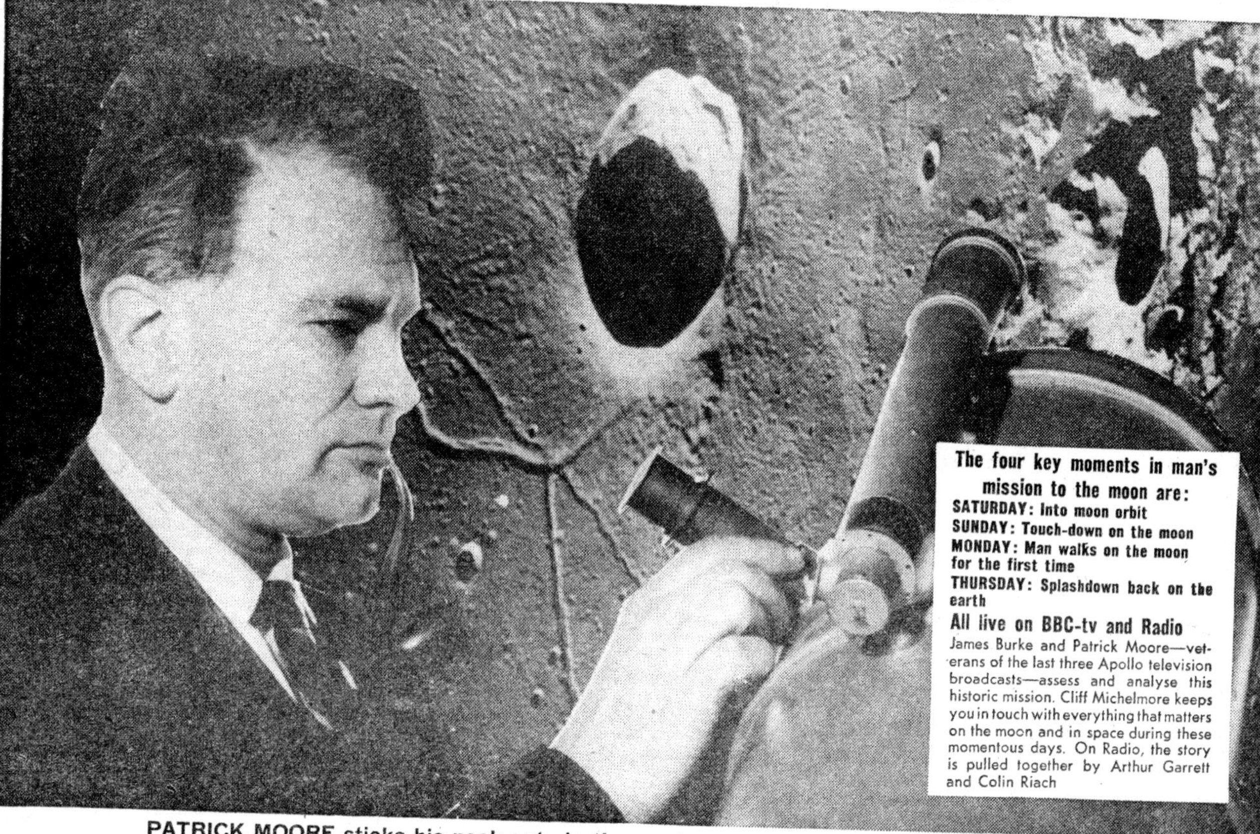

PATRICK MOORE sticks his neck out—in the week men hope to touch-down on the moon

SUN and MON

THE moon is our companion in space. It stays with us in our never-ending journey round the sun, and it is very much closer than any other natural body in the sky. For this reason it must be our first target, but in itself it is certainly not welcoming.

It has virtually no atmosphere; there is no liquid water, and the temperatures are extreme. This being so, it is clear that life, as we know it, is not possible there, and that travellers from earth will have to take the strictest precautions to guard themselves against the hostile environment.

Now that the first landing is so imminent, it is time to make an evaluation of what we know about the moon. In other words—what are astronauts Armstrong and Aldrin likely to find there on July 21?

The first essential is to see whether there is any danger of landing on soft ground. In the 1950s, and well into the 1960s, there was a theory—due originally to Dr. Thomas Gold—that the lunar seas, or *maria*, were covered with a thick layer of soft dust, so that any space-craft unwise enough to land there would promptly sink out of sight.

This idea did not fit the observed facts, and was opposed by most practical lunar observers, but not until the first successful soft-landings by unmanned probes did it finally die.

Whether there are any 'unsafe areas' remains to be seen. All the indications are that the surface is quite firm enough to support the weight of a craft such as the Lunar Module of Apollo 11, but we do not yet have full information about the nature of the rocks, and this is a matter of great importance.

There are two main theories concerning the origin of the moon's craters. According to some authorities, they are volcanic structures; others attribute them to meteoritic impact. No doubt both types of craters exist, and the point at issue is—which force played the major role?

Just at the moment, forecasts are certainly risky, because it is quite on the cards that the problem will be solved by the flight of Apollo 11.

However, I am prepared to go on record as repeating the view I have always held: that the main craters are volcanic. If so, then we will find there a great deal of volcanic rock such as basalt.

Since the moon has virtually no atmosphere, there can be no erosion; winds and water are absent. This means that the surface has remained practically unchanged for an immense period.

Much will be learned from studies of meteorites which have hit the moon—and will there be any of the strange, glassy objects known as tektites, found in certain areas of the earth, whose nature is still a complete mystery?

If there are tektites, their forms should show whether the moon ever had a reasonably dense atmosphere; a tektite assumed to have come down through the earth's air is 'aerodynamically shaped'—but as yet it cannot even be proved without doubt that tektites are extra-terrestrial at all.

However the moon came into being, there can be little doubt that its materials are of the same general type as those of earth. The idea that the earth and moon once formed a single body, and that the moon broke away leaving the depression now filled by the Pacific, has fallen into disfavour, but there is no reason to suppose that the two worlds are at all dissimilar in their composition.

Certainly it is not likely that there will be any spectacularly unfamiliar substances there. The chances of finding materials which would be commercially valuable, and worth bringing back to earth, are slender; but we must remember that as a site for a scientific research base the moon will be of inestimable value to mankind.

There remains the question of possible past life on the moon. If it ever existed, there would be fossils in the lunar crust. It is an intriguing idea, but we have to admit that the evidence is heavily against it.

Life is always slow to evolve, and on the moon it probably had no chance to do so before any lunar atmosphere leaked away, and the conditions became hopelessly hostile.

It looks as though the moon has been sterile throughout its long history; the story of lunar life will begin only at the moment when astronauts Armstrong and Aldrin land there.

Over the centuries there have been many speculations about what will be found on the moon. Some of these speculations have been sober and rational, others wild and improbable. Now, the age of speculation is almost at an end. The first on-the-spot surveys are about to be made, and specimens will be brought back home for detailed analysis in our laboratories.

The moon is about to yield up at least some of its closely-guarded secrets, even though the whole story may take a long time to unravel.

▲ In July 1969, Patrick previewed that week's manned Moon landing. He later conceded that the lunar craters were not volcanic in origin

▼ On 10 May 1969, Patrick's most unusual programme was broadcast, examining the beliefs of what he called 'independent thinkers'

RADIO TIMES *May 8, 1969*

He likes practical jokes and rides a bike that's falling to bits—yet the modest scholar in a shiny suit is one of the world's leading astronomical authorities

PATRICK MOORE
the man you expect to be unpredictable

Simon Campbell-Jones, producer of Can You Speak Venusian?—this week's One Pair of Eyes programme — writes a profile of the man everyone likes and nobody knows

COLOUR SAT 8.25

'ARE you a conventionalist?' asked Patrick Moore. 'I am!' We were out shooting the trailer for his 'One Pair of Eyes' programme.

Nothing, of course, could be further from the truth, as anyone who has watched his *Sky at Night* series over the last twelve years will know. It is his unconventional personality, bushy eyebrows, unruly hair, and infectious enthusiasm that have brought the series such popularity among millions of viewers. And yet very little is known about his unusual career.

For instance, he had what he calls 'an annoying amount' of illness during his boyhood. His heart insisted on 'playing tricks'; and though this did not stop him from receiving as much academic instruction as everyone else, it did mean a series of tutors and coaching establishments instead of Public School.

Only a year later he was fiddling his way into the RAF along with all the other young men at the beginning of the war. He knew he would fail the medical although he was quite good at the aptitude tests; so he arranged with a friend to do all his written papers while the friend dodged in and out of the medical cubicles pretending to be Patrick Moore as well as himself. He flew with the RAF as a navigator, no doubt using his already well-developed passion for the stars and things astronomical. He was also involved in what was often called the Department of Bright Ideas, which dealt with all sorts of schemes for winning the war—such as building a raft the size of England and floating it in the North Sea to confuse enemy radar.

He insists that he is only an amateur astronomer, but he is accepted as an authority on the subject of the Moon and planets—and certainly he knows the geography of the Moon better than that of the Earth.

His garden at Selsey in Sussex is littered with telescopes, and friends and visitors frequently pop in for a quick look. He drives a 1949 Ford Prefect—'the Ark'—and rides a machine which could just about be called a bicycle. As he pedalled off to the village to get a thermometer, needed for the film, bits of bicycle fell about in the road as the baggy-suited figure vanished round the corner. That shiny suit and the RAF tie are famous. He has been wearing them for as long as he can remember, and he is never to be seen wearing anything else.

His first book was published, he says, by mistake and since then numerous books and articles have flowed from a weird collection of ancient typewriters—he now hates writing in longhand. Some have been science fiction—'best forgotten'—and some science fact, the latest of which is a large, illustrated volume simply entitled *Space*. He is also editor of the magazine *Planetarium*.

He plays the piano in a competent but delightfully ridiculous fashion, and once he gave a piano recital in Torquay of the works of a completely fictitious composer which he simply made up as he went along. He also improvises his own title music for his film. The drawings for the titles are by Mrs. Moore, Patrick's mother.

He admits to the sense of humour of a nine year old and, when we visited a prep school where he used to teach, a spontaneous snowball fight broke out with Patrick giving the boys as good as he got.

Everyone who has worked with him regards him with enormous affection, and as an example of his incredible capacity for work let me quote one occasion. After a full day's film work we spent the evening stargazing in his unheated observatory and finally left him after midnight. The following morning we discovered that he had gone back to his desk, written a couple of articles and 'a few letters,' gone out again at 3 a.m., made some observations of Jupiter, and was finally up again before we called for him at 9 a.m.

His individuality and enthusiasm made him an ideal contributor to the 'One Pair of Eyes' series, and the ideal person to introduce us to the unconventional people he has met over the years. He shares their cheerful, good-natured independence and yet some of them are so far out on a limb that one begins to wonder if Patrick Moore is not a conventionalist after all.

1.50-3.0
APOLLO 11
Target Moon

APOLLO

Direct from the launching pad at the Kennedy Space Center, Florida—today's final countdown and launch which is scheduled to put two American astronauts on the moon's surface on Sunday evening

Introduced by **Cliff Michelmore**

Commentators in the Space Studio **James Burke, Patrick Moore**

Reporter at the Kennedy Space Center, Florida **Michael Charlton**

Produced from the BBC Apollo Space Studio in association with the European Broadcasting Union, the American Television Networks, the National Aeronautics and Space Administration

Also on BBC-2 in colour

See cover story and special feature pages 26-31

▼ In July 1969, Patrick and James Burke were the studio experts for the BBC's coverage of the first manned Moon landing

Patrick Moore and James Burke in the Space Studio—1.50

▼ The Birdman Rally challenged competitors to 'fly' 100 yards from the pier in Selsey, Patrick's home, without hot air or mechanical aid

5.15 *Colour*
Event

The Selsey Birdman Rally 1972
'This thing can be done!' said **Patrick Moore,** official starter and optimist, as 17 intrepid aeronauts attempted to become the first man to flap, glide (or even levitate) their way 50 yards over the sea.
Reporter ANNE NIGHTINGALE

Director PAUL DICKIN
Producer DAVID TURNBULL (from Bristol)

BBC2

Telly travel – Patrick Moore watches The Goodies *go into orbit:* 7.5

7.5 *Colour*

The Goodies

starring
Tim Brooke-Taylor
Graeme Garden
Bill Oddie
with
Patrick Moore
Corbet Woodall

This week the lighthouse-keeping Goodies lose their light in a fog, strike oil in a gale, light a match and go into orbit!

Written by GRAEME GARDEN and BILL ODDIE with TIM BROOKE-TAYLOR
Music by BILL ODDIE and MICHAEL GIBBS
Designer JOHN STOUT
Producer JIM FRANKLIN

▲ **Patrick appeared in several episodes of madcap comedy series *The Goodies*, including this one broadcast on 31 March 1975**

▼ **Renowned radio astronomer Martin Ryle reflected on *The Sky at Night*'s first 20 years on 20 April 1977**

44 — 20 APRIL 197

WEDNESDAY *tv*

BBC1

10.25 pm The Sky at Night. Astronomer Royal **Professor Sir Martin Ryle** pays an anniversary tribute to the programme which has brought about an increased understanding of developments in astronomy over the years

Astronomy has, from the earliest times, presented Man with the greatest of questions – the nature of the Universe and of his place in it. It also provided (until the last 35 years) the only method of long-distance navigation and so permitted, for good or bad, the interaction of different civilisations. Not until the development of the physical sciences did it become possible to examine the precise motions and the nature of the celestial bodies. The last 20 years have seen dramatic developments, mainly due to the extension of our observations to new parts of the spectrum, outside the band of visible wavelengths; the results have revealed entirely unexpected classes of celestial object which on the one hand have needed new ideas in order to understand their nature and origin, and on the other have provided the opportunity of testing fundamental physical theories.

Patrick Moore has, over these 20 years, succeeded in presenting, in a way which can be understood, these remarkable developments, which have depended on large optical and radio telescopes and on infra-red, ultra-violet and X-ray telescopes carried above the earth's atmosphere by aircraft, balloons, or satellites. At the same time 'The Sky at Night' has given an overall view of astronomy and has told us what to look out for when all we have is a pair of binoculars.

This is a remarkable achievement, and one for which we should thank Patrick Moore. He has brought to a huge audience some of the awe and wonder which early Man must have had in contemplating the heavens, but which is so easily lost in our modern society.

◀ Patrick about to be doused in water while talking to Eddie Waring on *It's A Celebrity Knockout*, a star-studded edition of the knockabout sporting contest, on 21 August 1978

21 August 1978

BBC 1

Some of The Lord's Taverners team who try to make monkeys of celebrities from the world of entertainment in It's a Celebrity Knockout*: 7.10 pm*

7.10-8.10 It's a Celebrity Knockout

Members of The Lord's Taverners challenge a team of Celebrities in a special edition of *It's a Knockout*
Taking part:
**Robin Askwith, Raymond Baxter
John Blythe, Tommy Boyd
Patricia Brake, Tim Brooke-Taylor
Paul Burnett, Eddie Capelli
Judith Chalmers, Jacqueline Clarke
Julie Dawn Cole, John Craven
Pat Crerand, Barry Cryer
Linda Cunningham
Roger de Courcey
Neil Durden-Smith, Jessie Evans
Tony Gale, Graeme Garden
Bob Grant, David Hamilton
Jenny Hanley, Anita Harris
Rachael Heyhoe-Flint
Frazer Hines, Derek Hobson
Kid Jensen, Barry John
John Junkin, Diane Langton
George Layton, Legs & Co
Liverpool Express
Linda Lusardi, Victor Maddern
Tony Mahoney, Mick McManus
Ann Moore, Patrick Moore
Eric Morecambe, Don Moss
Bill Oddie, Richard O'Sullivan
Nicholas Parsons
Lance Percival, Nora Perry
Magnus Pyke, Chris Ralston
Tim Rice, Cardew Robinson
William Rushton, Sheila Steafel
Ray Stevens, Mike Swann
Shaw Taylor, Meriel Tufnell
Bob Wilson, Norman Wisdom**
Introduced from
Fulham Football Club by
Stuart Hall and **Eddie Waring**
Referee ARTHUR ELLIS

Designer STUART FURBER
Director KEITH PHILLIPS
Producer CECIL KORER
BBC Manchester

▼ The 25th anniversary in April 1982 came as astronomers were looking forward to a future telescope in space

9.45* pm News

with Michael Sullivan; Weather

10.0* The Sky at Night

The Unfolding Universe
In this special programme to mark the 25th anniversary of *The Sky at Night*, **Patrick Moore** reports on what's happening at great observatories all over the world; he talks to space researchers and 'ground-based' astronomers, and his journey round the world took him from the top of Mauna Kea, at 14,000 feet above sea-level, to one mile down a goldmine in South Dakota.
This is a report not only upon what has happened in the past, but also a look ahead to the future, with the Space Telescope and other developments undreamed of when the first *Sky at Night* was transmitted.

FEATURE P6

Photography JIM PEIRSON
Sound RON KEIGHTLEY
Film editor KEITH RAVEN
Producer PIETER MORPURGO
(Repeated on 3 May, BBC2)
The Sky at Night 7 £2.25 *from booksellers*

25 April 1982

BBC 1

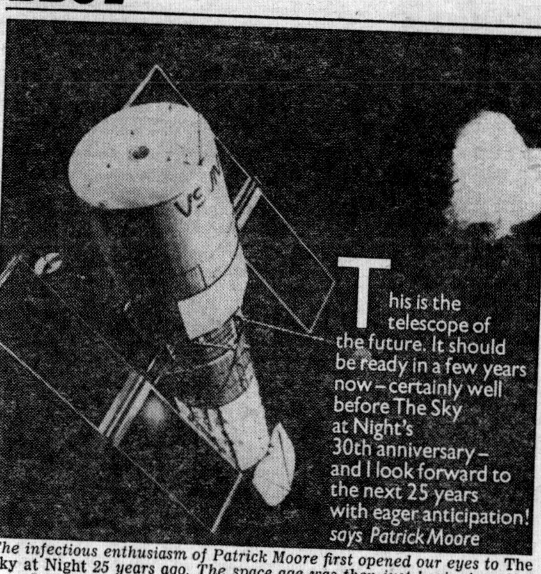

This is the telescope of the future. It should be ready in a few years now – certainly well before The Sky at Night's 30th anniversary – and I look forward to the next 25 years with eager anticipation! *says Patrick Moore*

The infectious enthusiasm of Patrick Moore first opened our eyes to The Sky at Night 25 years ago. The space age was then just beginning: 10.0

10.25 The Sky at Nigh

A Celebration

The Sky at Night is now 30 years old; the first programme was transmitted on 24 April 1957, before the space age began. Much has happened in those three decades. Rockets have been to the planets, men have reached the moon, great new telescopes have been built, and electronic aids have to a large extent superseded

Mark Gerson/Science Photo Library

After 30 years Patrick Moore is still starry-eyed about events in the Milky Way
BBC1, 10.25 pm The Sky at Night

▲ **By the time of *The Sky at Night*'s 30th anniversary in 1987, digital cameras had replaced visual observations for professional astronomy**

▼ **Patrick's *Radio Times* article in 1987 mentions Harlow Shapley, one of the great astronomers to have appeared on the show as a guest**

24 | 18-24 April 198

Heavens above, we're 30!

'The Sky at Night' began 30 years ago and things have been looking up ever since. Patrick Moore (below in 1961) remembers some of the stars who've helped it shine

A star is born: the presenter in 1961

The Sky at Night: A Celebration Friday 10.25 BBC1*

ON THE evening of 24 April 1957 I found myself in the BBC studio, Lime Grove, preparing to broadcast the first **Sky at Night** programme. At that time I knew even less about television than I do today; everything was 'live', so there could be no retakes, and I did not know what to expect. At least we had been ushered in by the brightest comet for decades, and I remember feeling that this might be an omen, though I had no idea then that *The Sky at Night* would still be running 30 years later.

Over the years we have had many experiences. I once swallowed a fly during transmission, and on another occasion reached the studio having taken some powerful sleeping-pills instead of aspirin. We have broadcast from aircraft and from the decks of swaying ships; we have been to the tops of volcanoes and we even made one broadcast from a goldmine at Deadwood Gulch, onc the country of gunslingers.

Astronomy has changed sinc 1957, and we have changed accord ingly. After all, when I made tha first broadcast the Space Age ha not begun and the very idea o reaching the moon was regarded as absurd. Moreover, exotic objects such as pulsars, quasars and black holes were not only unknown but unsuspected. We have followed all these developments, and we have always been ready to make changes at short notice. This happened last March; we had planned a programme about the movements of the moon, but altered it hastily with the appearance of the brightest supernova for almost 400 years.

Many famous astronomers have joined me in the programmes – some of them, alas, no longer here, such as Harlow Shapley, the man who first calculated the size of our galaxy. But others remain, and it is good to know we are still watched by a million or more viewers.

How long will the series run? This I do not know; certainly I will continue as long as I am asked and am able to do so. Thank you for watching – and see you next month! ●

**Saturday 25 April in Scotland. Patrick Moore's 'TV Astronomer: 30 years of The Sky at Night' (Harrap) is £12.95*

▲ A dapper Patrick observes the Sun with his 5-inch Cooke refractor in the roll-off roof observatory

Bruce Kingsley, who often visited Selsey to use the scope for observing Venus. "Patrick used it for many years for his observations of the planet. That was its primary use," says Bruce.

Views of Jupiter, Saturn and Mars also frequently graced the telescope's eyepiece. But in 1998, the instrument was nearly lost when a tornado swept through Patrick's garden in Selsey, ripping off the observatory's upper section. Patrick was out at a curry restaurant at the time, and on his return he couldn't believe his luck. "The tornado had gone between my house and the main observatory, knocking down a wall and dislodging the roof of the smaller observatory" he recalled.

Despite having no fewer than three reflectors, he preferred lenses to mirrors. "A refractor gives slightly crisper images than any reflector," he said. So it's hardly surprising that the fourth instrument in his collection was a 5-inch refractor made by the respected 19th century telescope maker Thomas Cooke. Patrick bought it from a businessman named Peter Sartori in the 1960s. It rested on a Charles Frank equatorial mount in a roll-off roof observatory, which Patrick designed himself and which was built by a local carpenter. "The Cooke gives lovely sharp images, so it's particularly good for lunar and planetary work," he enthused.

On his return to England in 1968, after working at the Armagh Planetarium for a short time, Patrick moved to Selsey. This was when he bought the largest telescope in his collection, the 15-inch reflector. "No one knows who made the mirror but George Hole re-figured it in the mid '50s and, of course, he was the world's best," he recalled. Unhappy with the original mounting, he contacted Dudley Fuller of Fullerscopes about a replacement. ▸

Patrick's telescopes

3-INCH BRASS REFRACTOR

Patrick bought his first telescope at the age of 11, a Broadhurst Clarkson 3-inch refractor on a pillar-and-claw mount. His first paper was published from observations using this telescope. In 2008, It was restored by Telescope House – the retail arm of the same company that originally made it.

12.5-INCH REFLECTOR

Purchased after the Second World War, Patrick's first reflector ended up with a Henry Wildey mirror and sat atop a Ron Irving altazimuth mount. Housed in a run-off observatory, Patrick used it to find and name the Mare Orientale. His Moon maps were also used by the Russians in their early lunar missions.

8.5-INCH REFLECTOR

When the Royal Greenwich Observatory moved to Herstmonceux, East Sussex, in the late 1940s and early 1950s it had a number of surplus scopes, one of which was an 8.5-inch With-Browning reflector. Patrick bought it and housed it in an octagonal observatory. It was almost blown away by a tornado in 1998.

5-INCH REFRACTOR

Made by the famous 19th century telescope maker Thomas Cooke, the 5-inch refractor came into Patrick's possession in the 1960s. Its mount was a Charles Frank equatorial design, and it was housed in a run-off roof observatory. It was restored and brought back to its former glory by telescope craftsman Steve Collingwood.

15-INCH REFLECTOR

Rounding off Patrick's collection was his 15-inch reflector, with a mirror that had been re-figured by George Hole. It was mounted on a Fullerscopes fork mount and housed in a rotating 'oil drum'-style observatory. Patrick mainly used it to study the Moon and planets, just as he did with the other telescopes in his collection.

Patrick's revolving, 'wedding cake'-style observatory was home to his beloved 15-inch reflector

The 15-inch reflector's rotating head at the top of its wooden body allowed viewing from different positions

▸ The result was a Fullerscopes fork mount, with the wooden-tubed telescope housed in a 5m observatory fashioned by a local blacksmith from an old oil drum. It was a 'wedding cake' design on its concrete base and its upper section could be manually rotated, allowing the telescope to be pointed at different parts of the sky.

The 15-inch telescope was also employed for lunar and planetary work – Jupiter, in particular, was a choice target. It was used extensively by Patrick and visitors to Farthings, including students and professional astronomers alike. On occasion, it was even fitted with scientific instruments by academics for bona fide scientific research.

Keeping the passion alive

In later years, Patrick's infirmity prevented him using his telescopes and observatories. But he wanted others to continue using them, and readily agreed to have them restored. Steve Collingwood, a craftsman working for Telescope House, fixed up two of the telescopes. The idea to refurbish the 3-inch refractor came about over a drink in 2008, remembers Steve, who has a particular passion for antique brass telescopes. The process of giving it a thorough clean took several months, and it was an emotional morning when it was finally reunited

▾ **Spit and polish: Patrick's 5-inch Cooke refractor gleams after being lovingly restored to its former glory**

with its owner. "He was like a kid at Christmas," remembers Steve. "You could tell he was a man with a deep love of this particular object – he said it was like stepping back in time to see it the way it was."

Steve also worked on the 5-inch Cooke refractor, which by then was in a sorry state. It was both a challenge and a great opportunity to restore another of Patrick's antique scopes, he explains. "Stripping it down was a job in itself. A lot of the screws and original components were missing. The complete rebuild took four or five months."

The 15-inch reflector's mirror was re-aluminised and collimated for the first time in 2005 by Mark Parrish, Pete Lawrence and Ian Sharp. As for its home, this would be restored three years later by a group of about 20 astronomers who got together on the Stargazers Lounge internet forum. They visited Farthings over a weekend, replacing rusted parts and collecting paint samples to match the dark, grassy green colour of the dome. The group later returned to refit the Cooke refractor's home.

The With-Browning reflector was refurbished by amateur astronomer Bruce Kingsley, who would eventually come to own it. On one of Bruce's visits to Farthings, Patrick asked if it could be restored, as it was by then dilapidated. "I said it needed a lot of work but it could certainly be done," recalls Bruce. "Patrick said, 'Excellent – would you like it?'"

Bruce was initially taken aback. Patrick had inspired him to take up astronomy at the age of 11, and he initially declined the offer. But Patrick insisted and Bruce subsequently spent 18 months getting the telescope ready for action. The mirror was re-silvered and the drive system entirely rebuilt, its RA and Dec. wheels made of admiralty brass. In 2008, Bruce had the honour of seeing his Kingsley Observatory in Maidenhead officially opened by Patrick himself. "The telescope has a very good pedigree behind it and I'm very proud to be the custodian of it," says Bruce. "But I will always refer to it as Patrick's scope."

Once asked to name the most stunning object he'd seen through his telescopes, Patrick unhesitatingly picked Saturn. "It is absolutely unrivalled – there's nothing to match it," he said. As for his favourite telescope, his response was rather more equivocal. "I simply couldn't choose between them – I like them all," he said.

▴ **A page from one of Patrick's many logbooks showing his favourite sight of them all: Saturn**

PATRICK MOORE X 3, TREVOR LITTLE

Musical MAESTRO

WORDS: JEREMY POUND

His love of music and performing led to many memorable moments

When asked to name his favourite pieces of classical music, as he was on occasion over the years, one work was notable by its absence from Patrick Moore's list. Hugely tuneful, gloriously late-Romantic, and by far the most famous space-related work ever written, one might have expected Holst's *The Planets* to have ticked all the right boxes – not least because one of those planets, Uranus, has a starring role for his own instrument, the xylophone. However, he preferred to turn his musical attentions elsewhere. This may have been because Holst's own interests were astrological rather than astronomical – each ▸

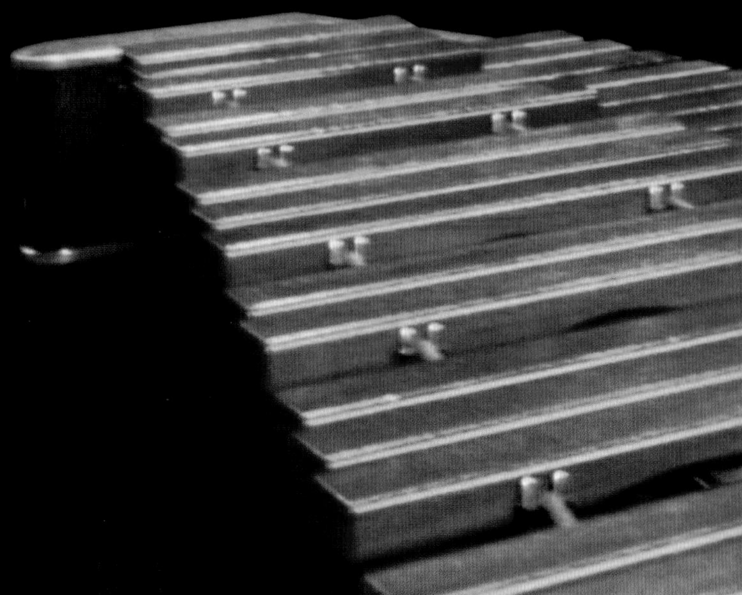

REX

▸ planet in the suite is given a mythological epithet. But it was more likely because Patrick's in-depth knowledge of the subject meant that he based his choice of listening purely on musical, not simply thematic, appeal.

That said, while he may have spent his life and career looking into the far beyond, his musical inclinations were considerably less exploratory, with the passion for 19th-century Viennese composers that he developed as a child remaining with him for the rest of his life.

"I think music provokes memories more than anything else really," he told *Classic CD* magazine in 1996. "The first piece I remember hearing was Johann Strauss's *The Blue Danube*. I remember that and the *Skaters' Waltz* which we had on very old, scratched 78s. I also specifically remember hearing Strauss's *Aquarelle Waltz* on my 20th birthday. I like light music and I'm particularly fond of Viennese music – another favourite of mine is Carl Ziehrer (1843-1922). I'm really a tunesmith rather than a heavy music man."

Modern, challenging music, meanwhile, would typically be greeted with some choice feline description. A 1995 work by contemporary composer Harrison Birtwistle was compared to "a catfight" while pop was "like tom cats being put through a mincer".

REX, CORBIS

▲ A self-taught pianist, Patrick wrote three full operas, an orchestral work and several shorter piano pieces

No surprises, then, that when Patrick composed his own music, memorable tunes and conventional harmonies took preference over the latest modernist thinking. He took his composing seriously, though: among a fair number of shorter works for piano or xylophone, one larger-scale orchestral work, *Phaethon's Ride*, and no fewer than three full-scale operas took pride of place in his portfolio. Two of those operas, *Perseus* and *Theseus*, have classical themes, though both with a bit of a twist on the mythological norm. Ever the sympathist, in *Theseus* Patrick portrays the Minotaur not as the ferocious monster that tradition dictates but, in his own words, as 'a delightful, kittenish little animal'.

Galileo Galileo...

For his third opera, Patrick turned to astronomy. His *Galileo*, based on Berthold Brecht's 1943 play *Life of Galileo*, enjoyed (at the initiative of Chris Lintott), a run of performances at Cambridge University in 2002 plus a subsequent performance in his own garden in Sussex. Here too, Patrick

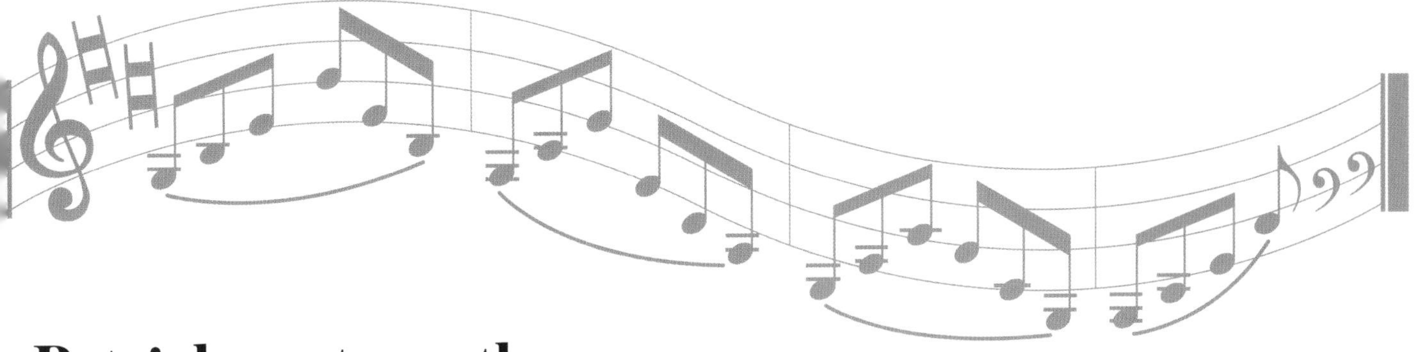

Patrick portrays the ferocious Minotaur as a 'kittenish little animal'

indulged in a little tinkering with the original plot for the sake of comic effect. Despite the mention of 'thumbscrews' and 'groaning victims' in the libretto, *Galileo* is a light-hearted affair and, in the Grand Inquisitor, has a baddie who might have come straight out of Gilbert and Sullivan (the only other operas Patrick appears to have had time for).

Composing largely at the piano, Patrick did know how to notate music on paper, though the handwritten page of his *Galileo* score reproduced in his autobiography suggests that this was a skill he wasn't entirely on top of – a couple of quavers go astray, and the emphasis on the word 'Beware' falls on completely the wrong beat of the bar. Still, it's clear enough what he meant to write and one imagines his performers would have had little trouble making the necessary adjustments.

While his music was never going to win any prizes for ingenuity, it is by and large well crafted and often great fun. His ragtimes in particular do a more-than-passable impression of those of the great Scott Joplin. Sadly, if you're hoping to potter down to your local record shop and find him under 'M' in the classical music section, you'll probably be disappointed. ▸

Patrick was particularly fond of Viennese music with waltzes such as *The Blue Danube* among his favourites

An accomplished xylophone player, Patrick performed on TV shows like *Have I Got News For You* and *This Is Your Life*

▲ William Herschel, the astronomer-composer, discovered Uranus. Patrick played his work on *The Sky at Night*

▼ Duetting with legendary performer Evelyn Glennie, Patrick modestly admitted "I wish I had a hundredth of her talent"

► Some of his music has been recorded – including *Phaethon's Ride* and other orchestral music, performed by the Royal Scottish National Orchestra in 1999. There was also an enjoyable selection of his piano pieces, played by Neil Crossland in 2004, but these discs have since disappeared from the catalogue. Instead, a hunt on eBay or Amazon may be your best bet.

Duetting with the Dame

While online, you may well stumble across footage of Patrick Moore, the musical performer. He could play, that's for sure – very well at the xylophone and quite ably at the piano too. By his own admission he was utterly unencumbered by stage fright, making several appearances on television – xylophone or marimba (basically a large xylophone) in front of him, sticks in hand. Though clearly happy to play amid the mayhem of Zig, Zag and Chris Evans on breakfast TV or even to tap out The Prodigy's *Firestarter* (check out both on YouTube), one suspects that the performance that gave him most pleasure was when he duetted with legendary percussionist Dame Evelyn Glennie at the end of the latter's *This Is Your Life* appearance. Patrick had the utmost admiration for Dame Evelyn. Describing her as "without doubt the best living percussionist" in his autobiography, he added disarmingly "I wish

trick studied transient features
 the Moon's surface and a glow
 Venus from his West Sussex
me, Farthings

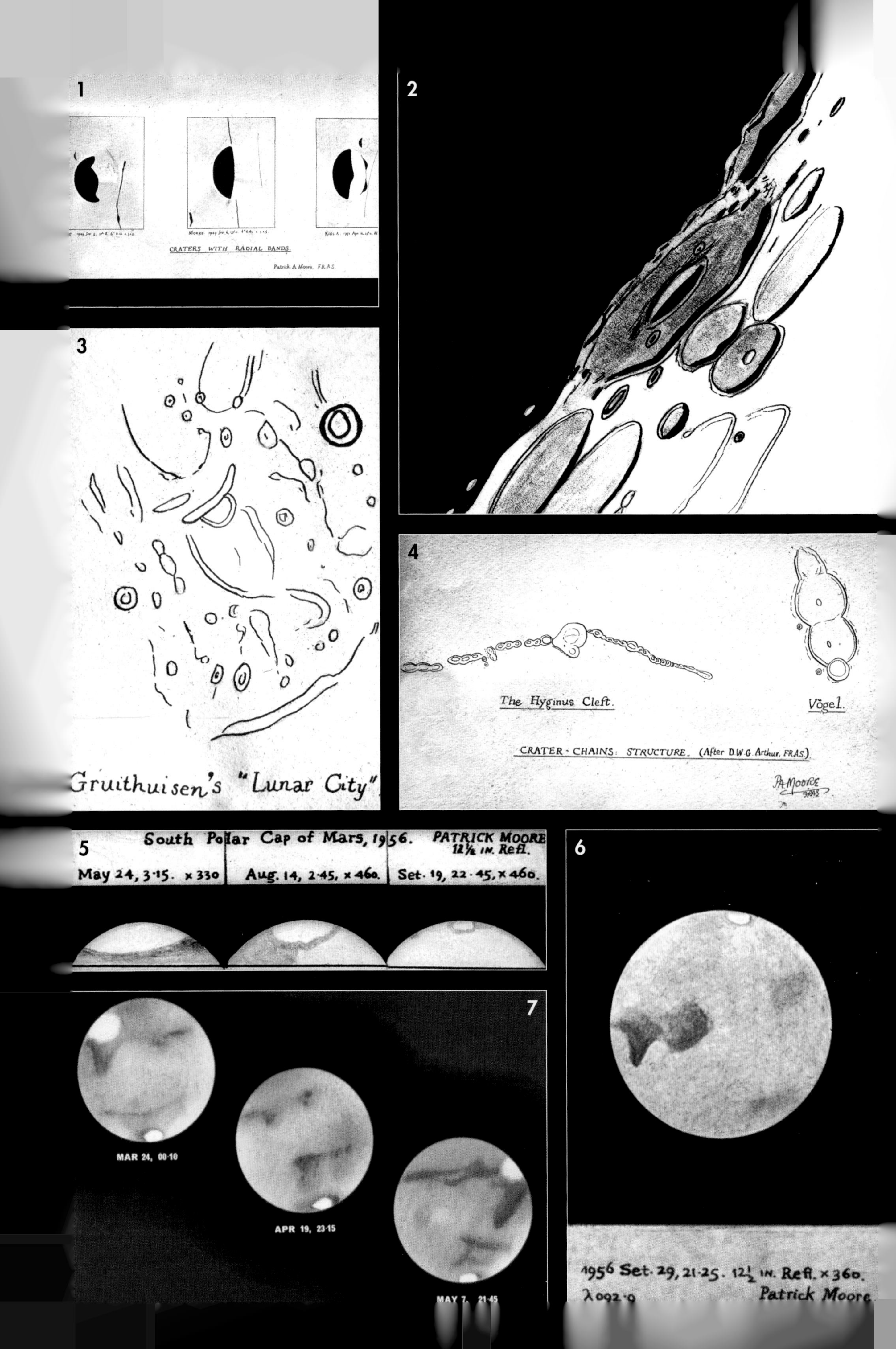
1
CRATERS WITH RADIAL BANDS.
Patrick A Moore, F.R.A.S.
2
3
Gruithuisen's "Lunar City"
4
The Hyginus Cleft.
Vogel.
CRATER - CHAINS: STRUCTURE. (After D.W.G. Arthur, F.R.A.S.)
P.A. Moore
5
South Polar Cap of Mars, 1956.
PATRICK MOORE
12½ IN. Refl.
May 24, 3·15. × 330
Aug. 14, 2·45, × 460.
Set. 19, 22·45, × 460.
6
1956 Set. 29, 21·25. 12½ IN. Refl. × 360.
λ092·0
Patrick Moore
7
MAR 24, 00·10
APR 19, 23·15
MAY 7, 21·45

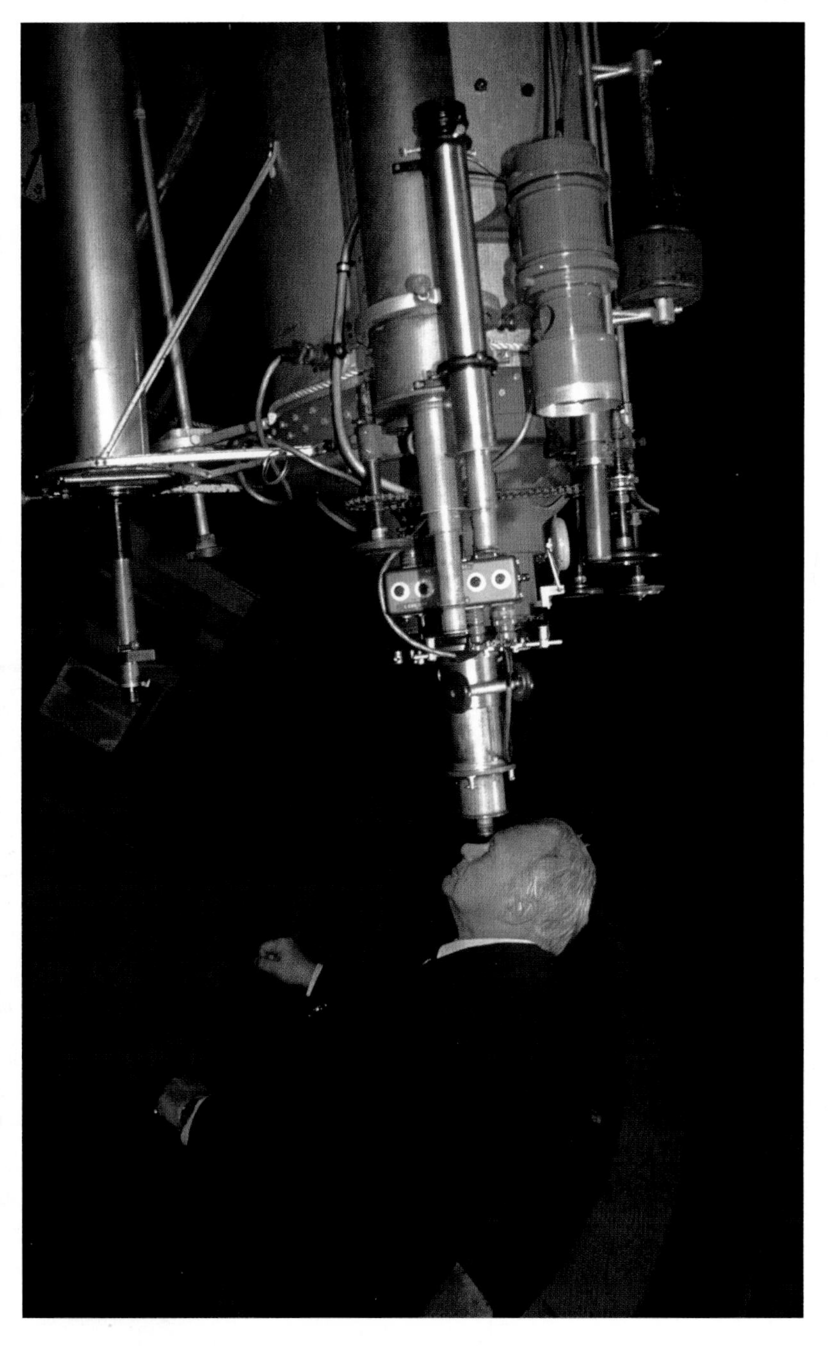

◂ The Lowell Observatory's 24-inch telescope gave Patrick an unmissable chance to view Mars in detail. There was no sign of the planet's fabled canals

▾ Olympus Mons on Mars, taken by the Mariner 9 probe. In 1971, Patrick monitored the dust storm obscuring parts of Mars's surface

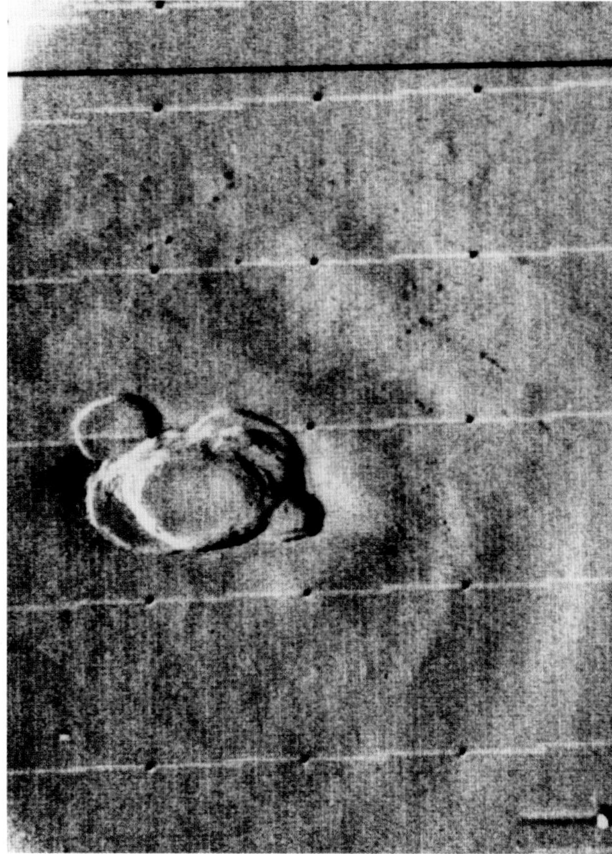

◂ **Patrick documented his observations of Mars and the Moon by making careful sketches:**

1. Lunar crater sketches from 1949 and 1957
2. Lunar crater Einstein, from 4 February 1958
3. Surface features north of the lunar crater Schröter
4. Drawing of Rima Hyginus and crater Vogel
5. Mars's south polar cap between May and September 1956
6. Mars showing its south pole, sketched on 29 September 1956
7. Dark markings ('albedo features') on Mars

▸ 19th century. If true, it would be evidence of life on Mars. Alas there were no canals but there was plenty of detail and dusky markings. Patrick also observed Mars using the 33-inch Meudon refractor near Paris, but again he could see no canals.

NASA calling...

Patrick's ability to report accurately what he observed, even if it meant contradicting earlier reports, only enhanced his reputation. He answered the phone at his Selsey home one day in 1971 to find NASA on the other end of the line. The caller asked if he would go to South Africa to use the Johannesburg 26-inch Innes refractor to monitor Mars for dust storms. NASA's latest probe, Mariner 9, had arrived in orbit but the planet seemed completely featureless. The only explanation seemed to be that one of the occasional, planet-wide dust storms had occurred. Mars was almost at its closest to the Earth but was not ideally placed for northern hemisphere observatories. What's more, Patrick was well versed in using the Innes telescope. He flew south and confirmed that there was indeed a major dust storm raging, giving NASA daily reports on the state of Mars for several weeks.

In 1995, Patrick made another great contribution to amateur astronomy, although he probably didn't appreciate its impact at the time. Like many astronomers, he was well versed in the galaxies, nebulae and star clusters that make up the Messier Catalogue – a list of 109 objects compiled in 1774 by Charles Messier. In an attempt to highlight the bright objects Messier had missed, Patrick came up with his own list of 109 objects and called it *The* Caldwell Catalogue (the moniker came from his middle name). Published in US magazine *Sky & Telescope*, the Caldwell Catalogue quickly became an established list of 'must see' sights in the night sky.

It's no wonder that Patrick inspired so many people to take up astronomy, both as a hobby and as a profession. But if it had not been for his accuracy and patience at the telescope, his television career would likely never have begun. Ⓟ

Here, there and EVERYWHERE

Snapshots from Patrick's personal photo archive

Patrick Moore loved travelling and thanks to his unique career, did a great deal of it. These photos from his personal archive give just a glimpse of his globetrotting over four decades. As presenter of *The Sky At Night*, he reported from the world's biggest observatories and brought great events like the total eclipse of the Sun into our living rooms. As a member of the International Astronomical Union, he travelled to a different country every three years to attend its general assembly. As a successful author, he was called on for publicity tours overseas. And there were speaking engagements as a lecturer on astronomy tours, often to see the Northern Lights. He also visited Japan to advise on a planetarium, flew to South Africa to observe storms on Mars for NASA and visited the Soviet Union to share his expertise on the Moon. But he was always happiest returning home to Farthings – his home in Selsey, West Sussex.

1960s

▲ Touring Moscow as a guest of the Soviet Academy of Sciences in 1960. He advised the Russians on potential lunar landing sites

◀ Preparing for a pioneering broadcast of a total solar eclipse from Mount Jastrebac, in what was then Yugoslavia

▼ In Prague for the 1967 general assembly of the International Astronomical Union

▲ Visiting a professional observatory in Japan in 1965 in his capacity as director of Armagh Planetarium

▲ Wearing a warm hat but otherwise underdressed for Yurgamysh, Siberia – prime spot for the total eclipse of 1968

◀ Showing the annular eclipse of 1966 in Armagh by projecting an image of the Sun through a telescope

1970s

▲ The 72-inch diameter reflecting telescope at Birr Castle, Ireland, in 1970. Patrick helped restore it to its former glory

▲ Taking the lunar rover for a spin with fellow TV commentator James Burke, prior to the launch of Apollo 17 in December 1972

▶ Visiting the statue of Nicolaus Copernicus in his birthplace of Torun, Poland, in 1973

1980s

▼ Visiting Clyde Tombaugh – discoverer of Pluto – in Las Cruces, New Mexico for an episode of *The Sky at Night* in 1980

◀ A mile below ground in Homestake Mine, South Dakota, in 1982. The world's lowest observatory searched for solar neutrinos

▲ In Java, southeast Asia in 1983 for the total eclipse of the Sun

1990s

▲ Back at Armagh Observatory to mark the institution's bicentenary in 1990

▲ With a model of Hipparcos at the Max Planck Institute in Garching, Germany in 1990

▲ At Cape Canaveral in April 1990 to witness the launch of Space Shuttle Discovery and the Hubble Space Telescope

◀ Dressed as a druid at Stonehenge for the release of a new set of commemorative stamps by the Royal Mail in 1990

◀ In 1990 Patrick also visited ESA's Space Research and Technology Centre at Noordwijk in the Netherlands. Here he is at the Space Expo

▲ Paying a visit to the replica of NASA's mission control in Houston, at the Kennedy Space Center visitor complex in 1991

▼ In front of the 25m dishes of the Very Large Array (VLA) radio telescope in New Mexico, USA in 1992

▲ **Three icons – Patrick Moore, the Great Pyramid and the Sphinx in Egypt in 1992**

▲ Admiring the Thomas Cooke telescope at Carter Observatory, New Zealand in 1993

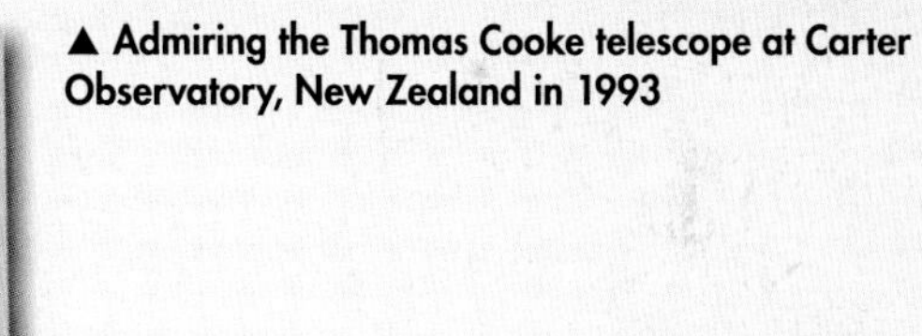

◀ Braving the snow in Alaska in 1993 to photograph the Northern Lights

▲ Preparing a newspaper with Dr John Mason (left, front) for the International Astronomical Union assembly in Buenos Aires, Argentina in 1991

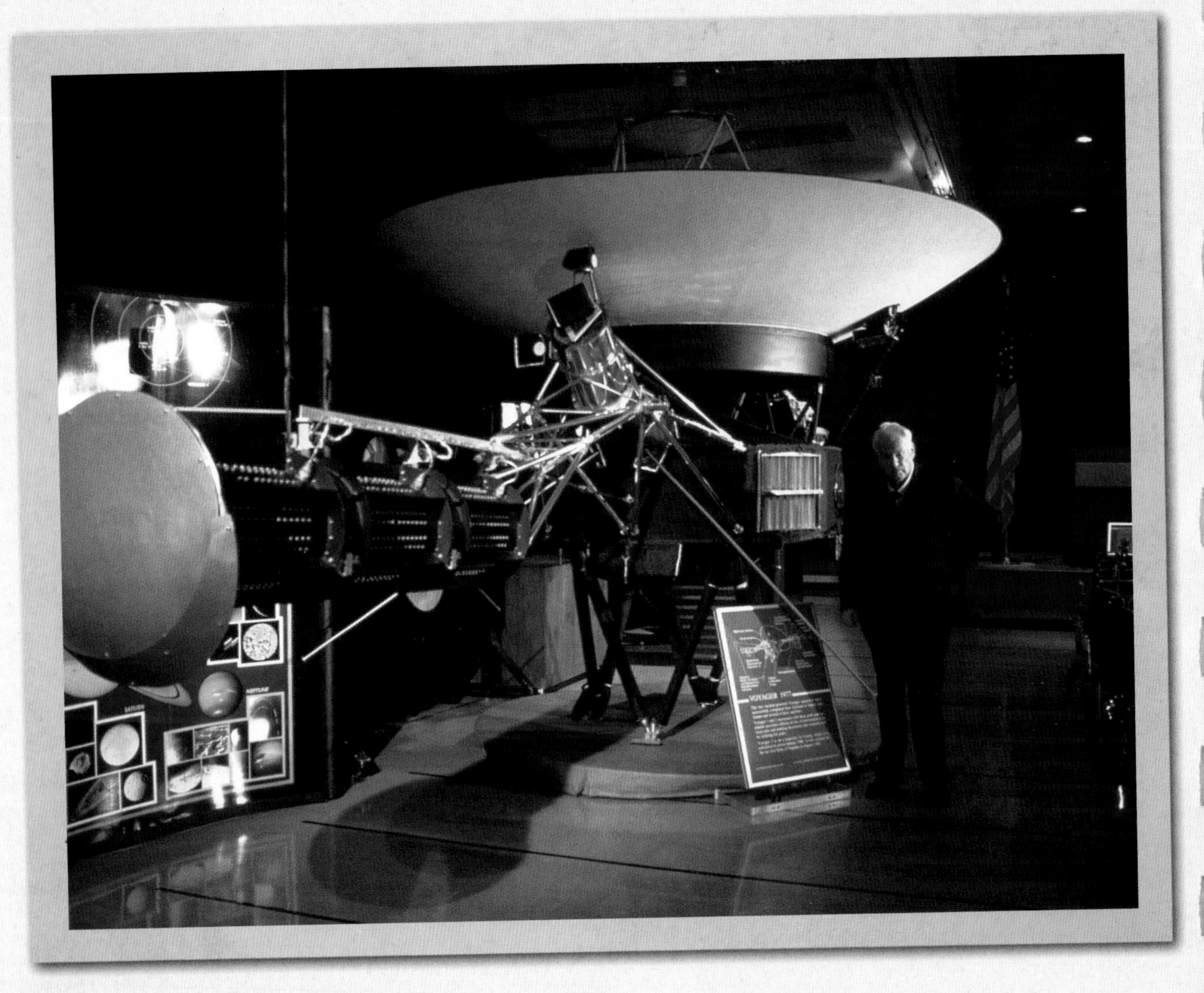

▲ With a replica of the Voyager space probe at NASA's Jet Propulsion Laboratory in 1991

▲ Standing before Meteor Crater, Arizona – one of the world's biggest impact sites – in 1996

◀ In front of one of the domes of Kitt Peak National Observatory, Arizona in 1996

▲ A return to the Republic Observatory in Johannesburg, South Africa in 1996

▶ Exploring the sights of Antarctica on a cruise in 1998

▼ Aboard the cruise ship Marco Polo as a guest lecturer on astronomy for a crossing of Antarctica in 1998

The last WORD

On the occasion of *The Sky at Night*'s 50th anniversary in 2007, Lord Martin Rees paid tribute to Patrick

"April 1957 saw Patrick Moore present the first episode of *The Sky at Night*. As it turned out, this was an auspicious time, because 1957 was a special year for science. In that year, Sputnik 1 was launched – an event that signalled the start of the space age. And Bernard Lovell's huge Jodrell Bank telescope – now acclaimed as one of the nation's iconic structures and still doing frontier research today – came into service just in time to track Sputnik's path across the sky.

I am old enough to remember these events and, as a schoolboy, to have watched Patrick's earliest programmes on the flickering black and white television that my family had recently acquired. Indeed, these programmes were among the influences that led to my interest in astronomy and there must be many others, of my generation and later, who were enthused in a similar way.

In the decades since 1957, astronomy and space science have advanced on an ever-wider front. We have witnessed Neil Armstrong's 'one small step' on the Moon; unmanned probes have been sent to all the planets; our cosmic vision has been extended and sharpened by space observatories (the Hubble Space Telescope pre-eminent among them) and by huge optical and radio telescopes on the ground. Patrick has reported on all of these, in more than 650 editions of his programme, and visited almost every part of the world where astronomy (and eclipses) are pursued.

What makes Patrick so special, and his programmes so engaging, must surely be his enthusiasm and his expertise. He describes himself modestly as an amateur, but his knowledge is encyclopedic and as up to date as any professional, spanning the cosmos from the Moon and comets to the remotest galaxy or quasar.

As a communicator and broadcaster, Patrick is a consummate professional. I don't generally enjoy appearing on TV, but being interviewed by Patrick is a pleasure – indeed, it was a privilege to join the roll-call of astronomers and astronauts to have appeared on *The Sky at Night* during Patrick's record-breaking half-century as its presenter and moving spirit.

▲ **Lord Martin Rees with Sir Patrick Moore at the opening of the South Downs Planetarium in 2002**

The Sky at Night is in itself a remarkable lifetime achievement, for which Patrick has put many generations in his debt, but it is only a part of his output. He has written many books, along with a steady flow of articles for newspapers and magazines. And he has given huge numbers of talks to schools and astronomy groups around the world.

What makes him even more special is the unsung efforts he commits to any cause that grabbed his enthusiasm, and his helpfulness to individuals. He bashes out responses to his immense postbag with his famous typewriter, offering information or advice. I'm one of hundreds – perhaps even thousands – of people who appreciated the personal letters they received from him.

We should salute Patrick, and thank him for the inspiring, informative and entertaining way he's helped so many of us to appreciate the wonders of our cosmic habitat."

***This article was first published in the April 2007 issue of* Sky at Night Magazine**